MOUNTAINS
OF THE
DRAGON

To Judith,
with my very best wishes

MOUNTAINS
OF THE
DRAGON

AN AUSTRALIAN SCULPTOR'S
ACCOUNT OF AN IDYLLIC,
SURREALISTIC EARLY LIFE
IN AFRICA

Helen Leete

HELEN LEETE

DELPHIAN
BOOKS

First published in Australia in 2009
by Delphian Books
(a division of New Frontier Creative Services Pty Ltd)
ABN 45 060 505 704
6 Merle Street, Epping NSW 2121, Australia
Tel: 61-2 9876 1050, Fax: 61-2 9876 4106

©2009 Helen Leete

National Library of Australia Cataloguing-in-Publication data:

Helen Leete. 1938-.
Mountains of the Dragon: an Australian sculptor's account
of an idyllic, surrealistic, early life in Africa / Helen Leete.

1st ed.
ISBN 978-0-9804668-2-9
Leete, Helen, 1938- – Fiction.
A823.4

Cover Illustration: Helen Leete
Cover and Internal Design: Ronald Proft
Subediting: Kristina Proft

Printed in China by Phoenix Offset

DELPHIAN
BOOKS

www.delphianbooks.com.au

This book is dedicated to all the characters in the novel.
To my beautiful mother, who died young, five years after arriving
in Australia, and my father who died many years later in 1986,
the year I wrote the first draft of this story.
To my grandmother and step-grandfather.
To my brother, Duncan, and my mother's sister, half-sister and
half-brother, all long dead, all while still quite young.
Ethel and Iris may well still be alive
As in the novel, I tried to contact them, but never succeeded.
To all of these, and all the other people in the story,
I dedicate this book with love and a sweet
and tender nostalgia!

CONTENTS

Preface xiii

1. A Clay Bull Page 1

"To make an end is to make a beginning. The end is where we start from."

T. S. ELIOT

In the mid-1950s a fourteen-year-old is packing up, because the family is going to Australia. Words and themes that will be taken up in the story are introduced. The opening words suggest that "they have chosen," not only a destination but a destiny. The clay bull is a sculpture.

2. A Farm in the Mountains Page 5

"What one wants to say is formed in childhood, and the rest of one's life is spent trying to say it."

DAME BARBARA HEPWORTH

Introduces an idyllic lifestyle among magnificent mountains, a child's extended family, her brown friends, the Italian prisoner of war who builds a magic fountain; and a grandmother who says, "You cannot cage a child's spirit just because you fear for her body."

3. Miss Pinkerton's School   Page 19

"to be nobody-but-yourself in a world which is doing its best night and day to make you everybody else – means fighting the hardest battle which any human being can fight"

e. e. cummings

A disaster! The child goes to school in London, and finds her cultural background, the stories she tells, as well as her aims and aspirations, are all at odds with conventional society.

4. My Mother and my Father   Page 33

"Knowledge comes but wisdom lingers."

TENNYSON

The complex and ambivalent relationships with her parents.

5. "Child of the Mountains"   Page 47

"I cry Love! Love! Happy happy love! Free as the mountain wind."

WILLIAM BLAKE

A triumphant return to the mountains of Africa, to be greeted at dawn by the Eagle, and a reunion with her nanny Dinah and friends Ethel and Iris.

6. The Secret Sculptures   Page 63

"Beauty is truth, truth beauty – that is all you know on earth, and all you need to know."

KEATS

The discovery, in a dark forest, of a secret graveyard. Of a stunningly beautiful sculpture and strange secrets about the past.

7. The Spirit of the Little People   Page 69

"See the mountains kiss high heaven."

PERCY BYSSHE SHELLEY

A terrifying encounter, high in a strange part of the mountains, far from the home range, with the legendary "Spirit of the Little People."

8. Sweets, Sugar, Coffee and Tobacco   Page 87

"Look and you will find. What is unsought will go undetected."

SOPHOCLES

A trip to the village to buy sweets to bribe her friends to go back to the mountain, to find the cave on the high peak.

9. The Bushman Stone   Page 95

"When we reach the mountain summits, we leave behind us all the things that weigh heavily down below on our body and our spirit. We feel a new freedom, a gentle exhiliration, an exaltation of the body no less than spirit. We feel a great joy."

JAN SMUTS

The child finds the cave, an ancient painting of the Eland, and in exchange for her offering, the Spirit gives her a gift of certitude, the Bushman Stone. The Eagle takes her on his wings in a swirling, swooping spiralling ecstacy of aerial acrobatics.

10. "Be a Sculptor"   Page 103

"Art is contemplation. It is the joy of the intelligence."

RODIN

Uncle Ben from England visits, admires the child's clay oxen, makes a bust, talks to her about sculpture, and introduces a wealth of new concepts and ideas. She is fired with the concept of becoming a sculptor. The Spirit of the Mountains tells her to "be a sculptor".

11. Separation   Page 113

"This is the spirit Beauty must induce, Wonderment and delicious trouble, longing and love and a trembling that is all delight."

PLOTINUS

A visit from an archeologist. At first a wonderful friend; then disaster. Her step-grandfather gives him the precious Bushman Stone.

12. Severance   Page 121

"The most beautiful thing we can experience is the mysterious. It is the true source of all art and science."

ALBERT EINSTEIN

The child is torn from her beloved mountains, from her Gran and from her lifelong friends, Ethel and Iris. Her parents come to fetch her.

13. The Soul of the Universe   Page 135

"The greatest danger for most of us is not that our aim is too high and we miss it, but that it is too low and we reach it."

MICHELANGELO

A strange train journey. A metaphysical station. A baby brother. School and the realisation that the only way to fit in is to make oneself dumber and dumber and dumber, to aim low. Paintings and prizes.

14. The Wisdom of the Ancients   Page 159

"Claim nothing. Enjoy."

EESHA UPANISHAD

Atom bombs, prejudice, a young man's arduous journey to recover the body of the old Bushman's wife; in England a friend with new ideas from India.

15. Men-an-Tol or the Stone-with-a-Hole   Page 201

"In ALL ranks of life, the human heart yearns for the beautiful."

HARRIET BEECHER STOWE

Another eagle dream, and a trip to St Ives in Cornwall to find the ancient Stone-with-a-Hole, which the old Aunt had long ago compared with her Bushman Stone.

16. Botticelli Hands   Page 209

"*The most important thing in living, is to reach out and touch perfection in that which you most love to do.*"

JONATHAN LIVINGSTON SEAGULL, RICHARD BACH

Playing the piano. (Hands are featured throughout the novel.)

17. The Myth of Eternal Return   Page 213

"*We shall not cease from exploration and the end of all our exploring Will be to arrive where we started and know the place for the first time.*"

T. S. ELIOT

The death of the bull.

PREFACE

This is a novel and NOT an autobiography. An autobiography requires a disciplined accuracy and a strict adherence to sequence and truth. A novel, on the other hand, is more like a work of art. A painter or sculptor might start from an actual landscape or a real figure, but as the work progresses the artist feels free to exaggerate, distort or alter small sections in the interest of greater harmony.

However, as can be seen from the dedication, most of the characters were in fact real, and most of the incidents and anecdotes did in fact take place, it is just that at times I felt perfectly free to play around with time and place. The first draft was in the third person, but when I transferred it to my first computer in 1989 it automatically changed itself to the first person, present tense, and the "voice" of a fourteen-year-old.

HELEN LEETE

"Our deepest fear is not that we are inadequate.

Our deepest fear is that we are powerful beyond measure.

It is our light, not our darkness that frightens us.

We ask ourselves, "Who am I to be brilliant, gorgeous, talented, fabulous?"

Actually, who are you not to be? You are a child of God. Your playing small doesn't serve the world. There's nothing enlightened about shrinking so that other people won't feel insecure around you.

We are all meant to shine as children do. We are born to manifest the glory of God that is within us.

It's not just in some of us; it's in everyone.

And as we let our light shine, we unconsciously give other people permission to do the same.

As we're liberated from our own fear, our presence automatically liberates others."

NELSON MANDELA

CHAPTER ONE

A CLAY BULL

"To make an end is to make a beginning.

The end is where we start from."

T. S. ELIOT

They have chosen. It is to be Australia. Our ship sails in a month. For a while it seemed certain that we would be going to live in Canada so enthusiastically did my mother collect books and brochures festooned with lakes and autumn coloured forests, and so eagerly did my parents read the glowing letters about the American way of life from my father's two cousins, one in America and the other in Canada.

Then they began to have doubts; my mother worried that the winters in Canada would be long and cold, and Father became a little irritated by his cousin Malcolm's materialism and boundless enthusiasm for baseball and gridiron.

When I felt them wavering I tried, half-heartedly, with a little flutter of hope in my heart, to suggest Africa, but even before I had uttered the words I knew it was a futile suggestion.

They hardly seemed to hear me, as my father declared that he could still play cricket and watch rugby in Australia. Once they started talking about Australia I knew, with a sinking heart, that Africa would be bypassed, that we would sail past the Cape of Good Hope, to Australia.

Now that it has been decided, my mother has immersed herself in the practicalities of the move. First, she says, we must sort out what to take with us, and throw away anything she considers to be rubbish.

Today she wants me to clear out my wardrobe; she has given me a large basket and a big black bin to motivate me.

"You have grown so much in the last six months, most of your clothes can go into the charity basket. Then all those boxes down there, I am sure most of them could go in the bin. We don't want to be carting all that paraphernalia half way around the world," she said before she returned downstairs to sort the crystal and the china.

The clothes are easy, I grab great handfuls of them off the hangers and dump them into the basket. Occasionally I feel a pang; some of the dresses which so delighted my mother have hardly been worn, and now it is too late, I have quite outgrown them. After all I am now nearly as tall as my mother. As I hurl them into the basket I hope the charity children will like them. More and more of my little girl clothes follow, all white, or blue or pale green, the cool colours my mother invariably chooses for me, until only my school uniforms and two new, awfully grown-up dresses are left on their hangers. My good day dress, dark, sober, navy-blue linen, well-cut my mother would say, but severely simple. My party dress is also blue, but an icy cool, palest of pale blue. The bodice is starkly simple, a straight boat neckline and little cap sleeves, but the skirt is very full, and has an underlayer of taffeta, which rustles quite seductively as I walk.

The boxes at first are more difficult, because I have always been a hoarder, a treasurer of mementos, odds and ends, bits and pieces, the kinds of things that my mother considers rubbish. The first box I pick up is labelled "birthday cards and letters." It is at the top of the stack because not so long ago I took it out to add the cards and letters I received for my fourteenth birthday.

They must all go, I decide, trying my hardest to be logical and cool, but succeeding only in becoming frivolous and detached; finding myself frivolously flinging things up in the air, watching bright cards and ribbons flutter like vividly coloured butterflies, floating, flashing, then falling into the jaws of the cavernous bin.

Followed by swirling, spiralling, tissue-thin white airmail letters, all Gran's letters, fluttering ghost-butterflies, wafting downwards, downwards, into oblivion.

For a moment I feel a searing wrench, but that first dumping has broken the ice, and I find myself becoming strangely detached, disinterested, careless; heaving boxes of treasures and mementos, and books, and notes, and poems and sketches, even my precious old rainbow-kaleidoscope rabbit painting, things that once meant a great deal to me, willy, nilly, up and over, into the bin.

At the last tin box I pull up out of my frenzy of severance. This one is different, this one has such a hold on me that I will have to sneak it into my suitcase, when no one is looking, I will never, ever, be able to bring myself to part with it.

Inside, are two thick wads of cotton-wool. (I can still remember taking the whole roll of cotton-wool from Gran's safety first cupboard.) Between the layers of cotton-wool are a rock and a dried clay bull.

There was a time in my life when I turned to them constantly for consolation in my misery, when I often felt an urgent, desperate need to hold them in my hands. For the last few months I have tried to resist opening that box, to avoid unleashing the pandora of memories they conjure up, willing myself to become cool and sensible, to focus on the ordinary, everyday, on the here and now.

But now I cannot stop myself, cannot help opening it, and carefully, oh so carefully, extricate the clay bull from the cotton wool.

"I made this!" I exclaim, with astonishment, looking at the little clay bull cradled in my hands.

"It is really very good!" It really is.

From its broad, planar chest, to its tapered hindquarters, from its long, fierce horns to the outstretched legs and whipping tail, it is the epitome of strength and contained energy. Despite its size, it seems bursting with life, to have a vibrant inner vitality.

A whispered thought flits through my wayward mind: "Long, long ago, Uncle Ben called this a 'bloody marvellous little sculpture'."

Gently I return the bull to the cotton-wool and pick up the rock. Not my special stone-with-a-hole, but the next best thing, another stone from my mountains, a stone which looks a little like an ancient palaeolithic Earthmother, the one they call "The Venus of Willendorf," though my stone was formed by natural weathering, not a sculptor from the mystic past. Yet to me it has become a powerful relic, a kind of talisman.

"This was part of the Mountains of the Dragon," I whisper to myself, as I caress it, turn it over, and over, in my hands; it fits so beautifully into my hands; and like magic I am transported back to my beloved mountains.

CHAPTER TWO

A FARM IN THE MOUNTAINS

"What one wants to say is formed in childhood,
and the rest of one's life is spent trying to say it."

DAME BARBARA HEPWORTH

The first part of my life, the miraculous, magical part of my life, was spent in those marvellous mountains of Africa. Rugged, rocky, hard, bare exposed mountains, of such beauty that my heart lurches just thinking of them.

I was taken to the Mountains of the Dragon as a baby, because the rest of the world was at war. Mother told me how my father sent us to take refuge on the farm in the mountains with my grandparents because it was so remote from a world at war. Father himself had gone off to the war; not actually fighting because he was in a medical unit, but "in the war" nonetheless. When at last the war ended, Mother went to rejoin Father, but I was left behind.

It was to have been for only a few months while Father finished his surgical studies and they found a house, and until rationing was eased; but, with one thing and another, the months turned into years.

Once in a while a fleeting uneasiness made me wonder whether I had been abandoned for some lack in myself, for some failure to live up to expectations, but these were only in rare, unsettled moments, and most of the time I was blissfully happy. I adored my grandmother, and revelled in the extraordinary freedom of having a vast, unending expanse of mountains and valleys to explore.

Some city dwellers might imagine a bleak and lonely existence, among towering African mountains, remote from the nearest neighbour, even further from the nearest tiny outpost, hundreds of miles from the nearest proper town. Yet I recall a warmly woven web of life in which every human being, in the homestead and in the circle of huts, and even every animal and every feature of the landscape was an integral part of the rich fabric of life.

The homestead was a hive of warmth and activity. Apart from my grandparents, there were my two young aunts and an uncle. Mother had been quite young when I was born and her younger sister had been at university, studying veterinary science, but often visiting. Mother's even younger half-sister, Kay, and half-brother, John, were there more of the time, coming home frequently from boarding school, or later, for longer and longer intervals between trying other interests, occasionally bringing young friends with them.

I had a wonderful grandmother, warm comfortable, and full of life. She was always busy, bustling around with a dozen things to do; not frantically, not stressfully; enthusiastically. Yet no matter how busy she was I could jump into her lap and ask her to read me this, or explain to me that, and she would stop and cuddle me, and read to me, as though she had nothing else in the whole world to do.

Mother was different. Although she was taller, there seemed to be none of Gran's strength and confidence, and I always thought of her as small and fragile, terribly vulnerable, and easy to hurt.

I do not remember ever jumping into her lap the way I jumped into Gran's lap. Perhaps I thought she might break like a porcelain doll, or that I might crease her silk dresses.

In the insubstantial way of the silk dresses, in those early days, when she was still on the farm with us, the wireless was another barrier between me and my mother.

That wireless, which Dinah, my nanny, called "the-box-with-a-voice" in her own language, seemed to have an extraordinary hold over my mother. Precious rationed petrol had to be used in the generator to make electricity, which could have fed the two light bulbs in the dining room. Those brilliant lights enchanted me, they needed only a tug on a dangling cord to conjure up their incandescent glow, but we were not allowed to use them except when we had visitors, the daily lamp-lighting ritual in the kitchen at dusk went on, because the electricity had to be saved for the wireless, for the voice that said,

"This is the B.B.C."

My mother would crouch, hunched up in her chair, tense, the static from the airwaves echoing the static of her anxiety.

If I came near, if I tried to question, she would beckon frantically, silently in mime, to Dinah, to take me away to go and amuse me in the garden. So I learned to watch, silently, unobtrusively, as my mother alone, or the whole family, all the adults, crowded, ears straining, around that disembodied voice.

At times the levels of my mother's anxiety would reach fever pitch. In a strangled voice, almost incoherently, she would say to the others, not to me, I was kept out of the way, "Heavy casualties, prisoners of war. He is with that regiment, in that place, he told me in this letter that came yesterday; he used our code, dots above the letters!"

And they would say soothingly, "That letter was written a month ago, he is in a medical unit, he is mobile, and could have moved on by now."

But she would be inconsolable, pacing around the house, smoking cigarette after cigarette, until the next time the wireless was turned on. I tried to ask Dinah what was happening, but she was deeply suspicious of this box-with-a-voice, it was bad magic, she told me.

"Mother is highly strung, like Fonk," was the explanation I gave to myself. Fonk was John's horse, his pride and joy. "What an inappropriate name for such a beautiful horse," the others had exclaimed, when he first brought home the magnificent white Arabian stallion.

All the other horses were sturdy mountain ponies, strong enough to cope with the steep, rough, rock-strewn terrain. This new horse was finely bred, tall and elegant and very highly strung. All the other horses would come running to greet one with a nuzzle, if approached with a carrot or a handful of government sugar, but the beautiful Fonk was so easily startled, so nervous that his eyes would flash, and his nostrils flare and he would go galloping off in fright, every time anyone except John approached him. At other times he would rear up on his hind legs, even at the sight of a little meerkat, rear up so high that I was terrified he would fall over backwards and break his elegant back. He seemed far too fine-boned for this harsh mountain country. I thought that he should only be allowed to gallop in the moonlight, along a soft sandy beach. I somehow knew that he was too beautiful and too delicate to survive for long.

Sometimes in my dreams, the beautiful white horse and my mother became interchangeable.

Apart from the immediate family on the farm, there were also "The Aunts". The one was Gran's widowed sister and the other, a maiden lady, an old friend who had been invited to come and recover from an emotional trauma, or illness, many years ago, and had simply stayed on and become a permanent member of the household.

Then too, for a few years, towards the end of the war, there were the Italian prisoners of war, although it seemed to me that these men were more like friends living in a stone room near the stables. Gran explained that they had been captured in a battle up north, in Ethiopia or Egypt, and had been sent south on the next ship, as prisoners of war with their captors who were going home on leave. They were sent out to remote farms, to help with food or wool production, instead of being confined to prison camps.

One was a small, dark, furtive sort of man, and all I remember about him is that he seemed desperately unhappy and hardly ever spoke because he knew absolutely no English. His companion explained that he had grown up in a crowded city, in a narrow street, in a building crammed with dozens of families, where life was enjoyed in the noisy milling congestion of markets and cafes, something I tried hard to imagine, but could not. The vastness and remoteness and the silence terrified him, as did the horses, which limited his use as a farm worker, because the men went about their business on horseback.

I found it hard to believe that anyone could not like horses, and even harder to believe that anyone could be terrified by vastness and remoteness; the very things I loved about the mountains.

The other Italian was quite different. His name was Landi, and he had light brown hair, and bright blue eyes. He spoke a little English, heavily accented but enthusiastically and full of funny phrases and I soon decided that I liked him. He was an artisan, he said, he worked with stone and cement.

He made me aware of the craftsmanship of the stonework in the house and the complex of stables, wool sheds, storerooms and barns. He ran his hands over the rusticated masonry, the rugged texture in the centre of each stone, yet so finely chiselled along the straight edges that there was hardly any need for mortar in the knife-thin joints. As skilfully executed, he said, caressing the fine mountain stone, as beautiful as anything he had seen at home.

He too, had no desire to work with my grandfather, so after a while he persuaded my grandmother that her garden, her pride and joy, lacked only one thing, the one thing that every Italian villa and every Italian town had, and that was a fountain.

So he set about making the fountain for the garden. We, my friends and I, had no idea what a fountain was. Gran's garden did not have anything as modern as a tap or hose or sprinkler. All watering was done with running furrows, as natural as miniature rivers. Furrows of muddy brown water running down from the dam, running to each garden bed, the flow of water directed by the gardener with spadefuls of soil. So we watched with fascination as Landi built a large pond of mountain rock, and in the centre, a conical pyramid of the same rocky boulders. Then he began working in concrete, making a large circular mould and then casting a huge dish shape of concrete, which took several men to lift onto the pyramid of stone.

By this time the war had ended, and the other man had been shipped back to Italy, but Landi wanted to stay, and was determined to finish the fountain, so nearly everyone on the farm was conscripted to help. Another pyramid of rocks, another dish slightly smaller than the first, and then yet another still smaller pyramid and pond.

At last the day came to fill it, and turn it on. Those of us who had lived most of our lives in the mountains had never seen a fountain before, and we watched in wonder as water flowed out of the pipe at the summit, cascading into the topmost dish, and then when it was full, it overflowed, over the perfectly level, perfectly circular rim in a fine curving translucent veil, a shimmering, rainbow-shedding, circular waterfall. Then that dish also overflowed, and the next, until there was this wonderland of water, dancing before our eyes.

Gasps of wonder and tongue-clicking hoots and haws of enchantment rippled around the gathering crowd.

I was utterly enchanted, dancing, skipping, circling, around and around the rainbow-shedding water, singing, "It is beautiful, so, so, so beautiful!" And the wind whipped wisps of mist that kissed my cheek.

Soon I was joined by a little band of followers, dancing behind me, chanting in their language, "It is magic, magic, magic! Landi is a magician. He has made powerful magic!" and as they danced they trailed their brown fingertips through the cool cascading waters.

To them it was pure magic, magician's magic, while to me it was a mixture of magic and Landi's knowledge; but then knowledge itself is a kind of magic, even the knowledge of pipes and pumps and craft and construction, electricity and ingenuity.

All the friends following me were brown. All the rich warm browns of ripe acorns, of ebony ornaments and mahogany furniture. They were the children of the native people who lived in a compound of circular mud and thatched huts on the hillside about half a mile from the homestead, most of whom worked on the farm or in the house.

Dinah, who for the first year or so had been my nanny, then later became Gran's cook, had two daughters to whom she had given English names, Ethel and Iris. They were a few years older than I was, my minders really, and so my constant companions. As a toddler, I am told, I was always running off and disappearing and the only time they could keep track of me was when I was firmly strapped in a red blanket on Dinah's back, but I could not spend the whole day strapped in a red blanket. It was then that it was discovered that Ethel and Iris were the only ones who had the energy to keep track of me, and the only ones who could steer me back from my wayward explorations. Ethel was wise and sensible. One could sense this even when she was little, and she seemed to grow wiser and more sensible with the years. She was also gentle and sensitive, and she adored my gentle sensitive mother, who in turn was very fond of Ethel. Iris was wilder, more self-centred, more adventurous, more like me really, perhaps because we were closer in age. As we all grew older the three of us did everything together, went everywhere together.

Then there was a whole tribe of laughing, near naked children, who led a carefree, unencumbered existence. Apart from occasionally helping with the herding of the sheep, or clashing cymbals to keep the birds from the grapes, they had nothing to interrupt their days, no school, no pressures, no knowledge of, nor curiosity about, the world beyond and below these mountains.

It was from them that I learnt to gather red earthy clay and make oxen, like the one lying next to me, still preserved in its nest of cotton wool.

It was with them that I explored the mountains. At first it was because we were fascinated by the giant mountain tortoises and we climbed into the mountains in search of them. These were not the flat, dull-coloured tortoises of the plains but huge, high domed creatures with black and gold carapaces. The fully grown ones were so big that we could ride on their backs. They were far too heavy to pick up, but occasionally we would carry a smaller one down and introduce it to Gran's lush vegetable garden. The tortoise would stay for a few days, then to our surprise, because we thought the garden must seem like an earthly paradise to a tortoise, it would lumber its way back into the dry and arid mountains. Sometimes we marked their shells with watercolour paint to see if they went back to the same place.

Soon we were climbing into the mountains for their own sake. Finding tortoises was incidental. One of the Aunts, the one who was only a friend of my grandmother, was horrified that I was allowed such freedom.

"I don't know how you can allow that child to go off with a bunch of blacks like that."

Gran gave her a withering look, so she tried another tack. "There are so many dangers; snakes for instance."

Gran had an answer to that one. "Mountain snakes are shy, and those children are a noisy lot. The snakes will keep out of their way. Far more dangerous are the complacent puff-adders which have made their home right here in the shearing shed."

"And what if she breaks a leg?" persisted the Aunt.

"That child is as agile as a mountain goat," countered Gran. "Besides I never let her go without at least four companions. Two to stay with her and two to fetch help."

"You simply cannot cage a child's spirit, because you fear for her body," said Gran with an air of finality; and I continued to roam free.

So, very early in life I was instilled with the idea that I was a free spirit! Imagine a grown-up saying, "You cannot cage a child's spirit because you fear for her body!" But then my grandmother was not like most grown-ups.

Outwardly she was a busy farmer's wife, but deep inside she was a Romantic; passionately devoted to the Romantic poets and painters of the nineteenth century, steeped in the influence of Wordsworth and Coleridge and Byron, Turner and Watts. She loved to quote those poets and painters who infused the natural grandeur of nature with spiritual yearnings, who believed that sublime nature could leave an indelible impression on the soul.

The mountains I loved to climb with my band of brown friends were so awe-inspiring that they left more than an indelible impression on me, they left an imprint seared into my soul. An imprint. A visual image imprinted! The idea of imprinting is not some weird poetic fantasy, nor some far-fetched artist's imaginings, though artists so often invoke their earliest beginnings. Even Michelangelo wrote that, sent out to nurse with a quarryman's wife, he "sucked in marble dust with my nurse's milk."

It is also a scientific concept! I know because we studied imprinting in Biology the other day! Of course I was already a convert, I had encountered biological imprinting very early in my life.

Once, when I was very young, on the farm in the mountains, a broody hen sat on a dozen eggs in a manger. Eleven of those eggs hatched within a day or two of each other, and the mother hen bustled and fluttered the chicks down from the high manger, out into the bright world beyond the dark stables. Gran and I found the remaining egg, all alone. "It is probably infertile," she said, more to herself than to me, and picked it up to throw it out. Just as she lifted it, I noticed the tiniest peck-hole in the shell, so she let me put it in a basket of straw and take it back to the house, and watch, enthralled, as the tiny chick pecked himself out of his shell. He was such an appealing little creature, so small and vulnerable and funny, so fluffy and yellow, that I kept him with me almost constantly, carrying him around in a furry old glove puppet or letting him follow me around the house. But after a week or two, everyone else started complaining about slippery, smelly plops on the highly polished yellow-wood floors, and then one of the old aunts slipped and landed on her bottom, so I was persuaded to return the chicken to his family.

When the hen and the other chicks came to the kitchen door for a some food scraps, I put him down gently in the middle of the brood, but he took one look at his mother and eleven brothers and sisters, all exactly like him, gave a terrified squawk, and turned around flapping his little stubby wings, screeching and squawking, back to me. He would not for a moment believe he was a chicken, he had been imprinted with my image so that he thought he was people!

It is strange the way things occur, recur, echo and re-echo throughout one's life; even little things like the imprinting of chickens! Last week, at school, we did an experiment in Biology, to demonstrate imprinting. The teacher (who has become a legend in the school for her annual "chicken day") ordered twenty incubated chickens, and twenty volunteers were given a chicken each to take home for the weekend. The next Monday, the chickens were all put into a chalk circle in the middle of the hockey field, and we stood some distance away, in different directions, and called for our charge. Every chicken had been imprinted, and went straight to the girl with whom it had spent the weekend. The other girls were really surprised! I wanted to tell them about zebras, but I did not. I have become wary of being thought of as a show-off, and try not to show off my knowledge any more.

Amazingly, dazzlingly striped zebras! Long ago, before I had seen a real zebra, I saw an illustration of one in a picturebook and I thought what a funny, inventive artist to doll up a dull, dingy donkey in harlequin fancy dress. Then I saw real zebras, mountain zebras, a whole herd galloping, undulating across the veld, the rhythm intensified by the repetitive black, white, white, black, contrast, until my sensory responses were dazzled and befuddled by the frequency and speed and the insistence of the rhythm, and I was mindblown with awe-struck admiration, thrilled to think that it was Mother Nature's exquisite inventiveness.

But why? I wondered, why such dazzling, beautiful patterns?

Only a wise old man in Africa could answer my wonderings. A

mother zebra, about to give birth, moves a little way from the herd, and when her newborn baby stands up, she goes to great lengths to keep herself between the baby and the rest of the zebras. One might think, he said, that this is to protect it, but it is to imprint it with her pattern. Have you noticed, he said, that each and every zebra pattern is different. So the mother's pattern is unique, and it is a matter of life and death that the baby is imprinted with her pattern. The young are often separated when the herd is startled by lions or hyenas, or when they stampede, or set out on great migrations. No other female will suckle or protect a stray baby, so it is essential for a young zebra to be able to find its mother quickly. Imprinting means that her pattern stands out crystal clear in his mind, and he goes to her unerringly. All the other zebra patterns will always look blurred and unclear.

People, it seems to me, can also be imprinted with their first impressions of the world, and things that happen to us when we are very young have a profound influence on the way we see things for the rest of our lives.

I feel that I was more than just influenced, I was indelibly imprinted with the breathtaking beauty of the Mountains of the Dragon, and the experiences I had there. Perhaps this is why in the country, amongst mountains, I feel an almost physical expansion of being, why my soul is attuned to the gentle music of what, to others, might seem profound silences, and why the claustrophobic cacophony of cities make me shrink and cower, and my spirit recoils in horror. Yet, perhaps to those born in a city, imprinted with the imagery of a city, what seems to me ugly and jarring, is beautiful and reassuring?

It seems to me now that my real life was lived in those mountains. I was so alive then, so aware, that I can remember with vivid sharp-focused clarity, down to the minutest detail, like a zebra baby remembering only its own mother's stripes, every image, every incident, even every scent and sound.

It is my recent life that is sometimes blurred with a kind of artificial play-acting unreality.

Not only did Gran instil in me a love of the earth, a love of nature and of mountains, but her love of books and ideas left a deep impression.

At night, or on days when it was too hot or too cold and windy to go outdoors, she would read to me. She always started with nursery rhymes and fairy stories, but as my eyelids grew heavy, and as she grew bored with the baby stories, she would sometimes reach up into her bookcase for one of her favourite poets, and go on reading, almost to herself; and I would go on listening and imagining.

Soon I knew some of her favourite and most frequently read poetry and short stories and fairytales and Greek myths and nursery rhymes off by heart, and began "reading" them myself, by matching words I already knew with the written words on the page. Then gradually, imperceptibly, this pretend reading, which was only memorising, seemed to turn into the decoding of a puzzle, as the marvellous perception of how words worked dawned on me, and I felt that I was on the verge of being empowered with a special, potent magic.

Then, just when I was on the brink of this mastery of the written word, Gran said, "You are old enough to go to school now. Your mother is coming to fetch you and take you back to London so you can start school."

I had only the vaguest idea what school was in those days. None of the princesses in the fairytales, nor wise men and women in the myths and legends that I enjoyed so much, needed to go to school; none of my brown friends had ever been to school. I assumed that John would be the best one to ask because he had not many months before returned from boarding school.

"What's school?" I asked him.

"At school you will learn to read every book in the whole world," he said, teasing my inquisitiveness and curiosity and incessant questions, "and to be so clever that you know everything there is to know in the whole world. Then you won't have to always ask why, what and how come, all the time."

"Wow!" I said, naively, not for a moment grasping that he was teasing me. "Wow!" not realising that he himself had, in the last few months, become disillusioned about how little school had taught him about life itself.

The day he had written his last exam he and his best friend had gone off and enlisted, their imaginations and patriotism fired by seeing General Smuts at the bioscope, inspired by his words about valour and courage. They were both only seventeen, but they fibbed about their ages because they were scared the war would end before they could get there. In his naive, farm imagination he had pictured himself bravely going to war with his beautiful horse Fonk. He had been shipped off to Italy, Landi's homeland, where all he had seen was suffering and misery and starving children, chaos and cold and squalor, before he was wounded and sent home again. So when he said that school taught one everything there is to know in the whole world he was being ironic, seeing in me his own naivety, as much as teasing my incessant "Why? what? and how come?" But of course I did not realise that then.

So with naive, *"plaas jaapie"* innocence, I approached, like a lamb to the slaughter, willingly and with eager anticipation, this new experience called "school".

CHAPTER THREE

Miss Pinkerton's School

"to be nobody-but-yourself in a world which is doing its best

night and day to make you everybody else – means fighting

the hardest battle which any human being can fight"

e. e. cummings

In London, Mother stopped the car in the circular driveway at Miss Pinkerton's School. I looked up at the classic Georgian house that had been converted into a private preparatory school and thought, "This looks like a good place for learning to read all the books in the world."

Mother took me in to meet Miss Pinkerton, who, after a few questions said, "I'll take you down to meet Miss Ashburn, your teacher."

Miss Ashburn was at the kitchenette in the staff common room making herself a cup of tea. She spun around as Miss Pinkerton entered, and stood with her back against the bench. I felt that she was trying to hide something.

Miss Ashburn, I decided, had been aptly named. I was used to people being given names that suggested their physical appearance; I was sometimes called, in Xhosa, "the-little-miss-n'kosi-with-the-white-head." Miss Ashburn had ash-coloured hair, all the ash greys one finds in day-old ash, from silvery white to deep grey, her face was ashen pale, her eyes were pale ash-grey and even her dark grey dress was the colour of charcoal.

"I'll take you out to meet some children in your class," said Miss Ashburn, as soon as Miss Pinkerton had left. As she moved forward I saw that it was a cigarette in an ashtray that she had been concealing, and that by now it had a long ash grey, ashen tip.

I was beginning to feel like the parcel in a game of pass-the-parcel, having, in the space of a few moments been passed from my mother to Miss Pinkerton, to Miss Ashburn and now to some children. Nonetheless I followed Miss Ashburn eagerly into the playground at the back of the building. She went straight to a group of boys and girls playing near the door.

"This is a new girl in our class," she said. "She's from Africa," and she hurried back to her tea and cigarette.

The children stopped playing and came and stood in a circle, eyeing me in silence, the way dogs circle a newcomer, hackles bristling. I almost expected them to come and sniff at me. At last a little boy spoke up.

"I've heard of Africa," he said. "It's dark there. My father calls it darkest Africa. And there are jungles and vines everywhere. Deep, dark jungles." He shuddered at his own description.

"Yes," piped in one of the girls, "And tigers. Lots and lots of tigers in the jungle, and lions and elephants!"

"Did you live in a tree house in the jungle?" asked the first boy.

"Of course not," I replied "I lived in a big house built of mountain stone, and there wasn't any jungle, just great rocky mountains."

"And tigers? Were there tigers?" asked the little girl.

"No, of course not silly!" I replied. "There are no tigers in Africa and no lions any more where I lived. We once found the spoor of a big cat, and the old grandfather of my friends said it was a mountain leopard, but I never saw it."

"There are so, tigers!" retorted the girl.

"There are so dark jungles, my father told me," added the boy.

"There are not!" I cried.

"You're a liar!" shouted the boy.

"I'm not a liar!"

"You are a liar!" chorused all the group.

Just then the bell rang, and various teachers came out and stood at different doors, while troops of children sorted themselves into their class group.

"The new girl is a liar, Miss Ashburn," said the boy but the teacher ignored him and clapped her hands.

"Into crocodile file, children." I had not the faintest idea what crocodile file meant, but the other girls and boys in my class were falling into an orderly double file, holding hands with their partners. I was left standing, gaping, until by the time I joined the end of the line, there was no one else to be my partner, and so I had to file into the classroom alone at the end of the crocodile's tail.

Never mind, I said to myself, now I am going to learn to read any book I want to. But we did nothing of the kind. There were all sorts of activities, but not a book was opened. After a few hours, I went up to the teacher.

"Please, Miss Ashburn, when are we going to read?"

"You are not ready for reading yet," was her answer.

An hour later, I tried again. I thought I would make it a statement rather than a question. The other children were all threading beads, big wooden beads, a ridiculous past-time I thought, seeing that Dinah had already taught me to thread tiny glass beads.

So I went and stood in front of the teacher and said firmly,

"I am ready to read now."

"Don't be cheeky," said Miss Ashburn, so I had to go back to the monotonous task of threading beads.

The next few days were no better, and I was miserable and frustrated.

"Mother, my teacher won't teach me to read," I complained.

"Your teacher knows best," said Mother.

Gran, I thought, would have taken my side, not the teacher's.

"Then you could teach me," I suggested.

"Oh no! I might teach you the wrong way. Your teacher is properly trained to teach you the right way."

I wondered how there could possibly be a right way and a wrong way to read. Surely, I pondered to myself, reading was just reading, knowing what the words said.

So, the next day, I asked Miss Ashburn, "What is the difference between the right way to read, and the wrong way?"

Miss Ashburn must have been sick and tired of my constant requests about learning to read, so she shrugged impatiently, "Come along, you can join Miss Brown's class, they are reading already," and she marched me into the classroom next door.

Miss Brown did not seem thrilled to have me, muttering something about oversize classes. Nonetheless, she handed me a reading primer and then went back to writing letters on the board. She wrote an "S"; and all the children started hissing like snakes "s,s,s,s," they said. Then she wrote a "T" and they all went "t,t,t,t,t," like woodpeckers tapping at a tree-trunk.

"Now open your books," said Miss Brown.

On the first page was a picture of a cat sitting on a mat. Underneath in very large lettering were the words:

"The cat sat on the mat."

Miss Brown read it first, and then each pupil in turn. When it came to my turn, I was choking back tears, stinging, salt-bitter tears of frustration.

"What's wrong?" said Miss Brown. "Surely you can read that. The – cat – sat – on – the – mat," she repeated painstakingly slowly. "Can't you see the picture?"

That was the point, I thought. What is the point of reading what was already obvious in the picture? Reading was meant to convey ideas and images that you had to imagine in your mind.

At last I found my voice, "This is such a plain and silly book, I want to learn to read big words, and exciting stories," I said candidly.

Gran had been very strict about telling the truth.

"What a rude and precocious child!" said Miss Brown going beet-root red, so that her face was brighter than the cerise and orange floral dress she wore.

So I was marched back to Miss Ashburn's room, where she was reading the class a story.

I loved stories; except that this was not so much a story as a detailed account of a day in the life of an ordinary (very ordinary) child. The language was ordinary and factual, the anecdotes humdrum and unextraordinary. It seemed to be heading the same way as the story we had been read the week before, which was about going to the dentist.

I had not the slightest idea that there was a fashion for kitchen sink dramas, nor that there was a fashionable theory that children should only be fed literature that related directly to their everyday environment, and dealt only with familiar situations they were likely to encounter in everyday life. I had been brought up on far-fetched fantasies, fairytales and fables.

When Miss Ashburn had read the dentist story I had eagerly await-ed something dramatic: the dentist turning into a frog, or a fairy zoom-ing in through the window to rescue Peter and Penny, by tapping the chair with her magic wand and turning it into a flying carpet. Slowly, sadly I realized that this was a real life story, so less avidly, but still inter-ested I waited for some realistic shrieking and ouching; but to no avail. The dentist remained blandly kind and gentle, Peter and Penny blandly brave. The postmistress, butcher and cobbler in today's story seemed even more inclined towards bland niceness.

Sitting in the back row, I put my hand up to my mouth and yawned.

"What is the matter now? Do you find this story as boring as Miss Brown's reader?" snapped Miss Ashburn.

"Yes," I said frankly and honestly. After all Gran always insisted that one should tell the truth.

Unlike Miss Brown's beetroot-faced reaction, Miss Ashburn went an even paler shade of ash-grey.

"Perhaps you could tell a more interesting story." Her voice was icily sarcastic.

"Yes, I would love to," I replied eagerly, oblivious to the irony, and taking it at face value, as an invitation, pulling a stool over to the front of the semi-circle of boys and girls. How could these poor children pos-sibly think that getting up in the morning, having breakfast, and then going shopping was a story?

I would tell them a real story, the story of *The Odyssey*, of Penelope weaving and Circe with snakes in her hair, of giant waves and caves, of small ships in stormy seas, swept towards sirens and sea-monsters, of wise Mentor and Athena. But, though the pictures were vividly flashing through my mind, I was no Homer, and I did not have the words, the language to tell them the story.

So I settled for an easier task, a story I had told among children before, a story of the kind I heard my brown friends so often tell around the fire in the evenings, a comedy to make them laugh.

Now, in the years since then, I have read the Brer Rabbit tales and I would say the stories we told around the fire were the very distant cousins of those stories. The repertoire of the story-tellers around the fire was basically simple, but because the tales were never written down, they were subjected to infinite variations, at the whim of the individual teller.

Nonetheless, they all followed a similar pattern: the characters were animals, almost all of whom were "goodies", but there always had to be one "baddie". In our circle the poor old jackal invariably and inevitably drew the short straw and was given the role of the villain.

I began my story acting and miming my characters: the sly, conniving jackal, with his long, cruel jaw, and beady eyes, stealthily stalking his prey. The little, wide eyed bushbaby, cowering in the tree, until she was captured by the jackal, and stuffed into a big black sack; the dassie, fast as lightning, diving for his hole, but outwitted, outsmarted, lured out again by the wily old jackal, and being shoved into the blackness of a sack. Most fun of all to mimic, to an audience who had never seen one, was the almost-human little meerkat, standing up on his hind legs like a person, swivelling his neck around, so alert, so aware that he was almost impossible to outwit, but in my story he was so busy signalling a warning to the other small animals, that the jackal managed to snatch him too, and stuff him into the sack. The villain seemed to be outwitting his victims at every turn, and every time a bushbaby, or a Grant's

Gazelle, or a brave little meerkat was stuffed into the sack by the cruel, hungry jackal there would be a gasping intake of breath, and a quiver of apprehension would ripple around the circle of listeners.

I was beginning to enjoy myself, to feel that school was not such a bad place after all, to revel in my captive audience, even though I knew that my imitation of the various animals was not nearly as good as my brown friends, who had an uncanny insight into the body movements of all creatures, who had seemed in the moonlight to almost become the animal they were mimicking.

"Soon the jackal had a whole sackful of little victims, and started looking for a place to eat them.

" 'I know just the perfect spot,' said the wily baboon, 'a secret picnic spot in the forest, that no one knows about,' and, pretending to be reluctant to divulge this secret place, he gave the jackal directions on how to get there.

"Then the baboon and the other animals ran ahead, the little humming bird flew, even faster, to the quiet, secret place in the forest where the elephant had his daily nap, hovering about the elephant's great ear, whistling, 'Wake up, wake up, we need your help. I'll tell you what we want you to do. We'll signal when!'

"Then the other animals arrived, and draped the elephant with vines and flowers, quickly, just before the jackal arrived."

As I built up to the finale of my story, I stopped acting, stopped mimicking the characters. I clambered up onto my stool, stood above everyone else, and let the words flow, signposts for their imaginations.

I described the jackal arriving, sitting on the log that had been placed there for him, leaning back against what he thought was a tree trunk, but was really the hind leg of the elephant, smacking his lips as he drew the quavering bushbaby out of the sack, held her high above his head, and then opened wide his great gaping jaw, red tongue dripping saliva, cruel rows of jagged teeth glinting in the sunlight.

I was no longer mimicking my characters, but some of the children were. Their eyes were as wide, as round, as frightened as round bushbaby eyes, others opened their mouths wider, wider, wider, as I described the jackal tilting back his head and stretching open his huge jaws about to swallow whole the poor little creature held aloft above his open mouth.

I stood stock still, drawing out the horrified silence.

"And then..." I said, in little more than a whisper, "and then..." much louder, "the elephant shat!"

Now, at this point, around the fireside, all the tension would explode into laughter, my little brown friends would roll in the aisles, or at least in the dust, in mirth, slapping their thighs, as peals of infectious laughter rolled around and around the fire. From this point on the listeners took over from the story-teller, describing the splat into the gaping jaws, the smell, the humiliation and discomfort of the villain in vivid detail, and each comment would be greeted by renewed shrieks of laughter, until the adults would come over; and, overcome by the infectious mirth, would join in the laughter, until all the hills and mountains echoed the merriment.

This time, however, I was denied the warmth and companionship that comes with shared laughter.

As I reached the climax of my story, Miss Ashburn shot upright.

"Stop!" she cried her ashen face paler than ever. "Stop at once. We do not tell THAT sort of story in THIS kind of school."

I was dumbstruck. I felt as though I had been slapped in the face, but I could not understand why.

The other children were also struck dumb, so that the wonderful silence of anticipation was transformed into a dreadful silence of humiliation.

Now it seems to me that in almost every example of comedy I have since seen, from vaudeville comics to circus clowns, the stock-in-trade comedy standby is the pie-in-the-face. No matter how often it happens, no matter how predictable (in fact, it seems, the more often, and the more predictable the better), I have never seen it fail to bring a laugh. In those days I was ignorant and naive and stupid enough to think my story was just a much more basic, much more down-to-earth variation on the pie-in-the-face routine.

I do not know how long I would have stood there, rigid, up on my stool, feeling utterly exposed, utterly humiliated, utterly uncomprehending, if the bell had not rung at that moment. With an exhalation of tension, all the other children leapt up, fetched their lunch-boxes from their suitcases and spilled out into the playground. I followed slowly, still baffled and confused about what had just happened.

Two little boys confronted me as I walked out.

"You're rude," said the first.

"Yeah, you tell rude stories about poo," sneered the second.

"So do you," I retorted, "I heard you in the playground yesterday."

"But not in front of the teacher, stupid!"

Now I was hurt enough at being called rude. But stupid! That was far, far worse, the ultimate insult. I had never been called stupid before in my life! I gave the boy a shove, and because he was caught off-balance, and was not expecting a reaction, he sat down rather heavily on his well-padded rear.

"You hit my friend," shouted the first boy and dealt me a stinging blow to the side of the head.

I had never ever been in a physical tussle before, and rather surprised myself with an instant reaction, as I flew at my assailant, arms flailing, and legs kicking. Children gathered around, but before long Miss Ashburn intervened.

"Stop it! Stop it at once! I don't know what is wrong with you colonials. You go out and mix with black savages and end up with their uncivilised manners!"

Once more I was stunned. I just stood there, with the bruised eye throbbing, stock still, unable to move.

Gradually, the other children drifted off, resumed their games or sat in circles to eat their lunch. I longed to join them, but I could not move. I looked down at my lunch-box lying open at my feet, my sandwiches scattered in the dust, but I could not bring myself to retrieve them. My throat constricted, I could not have eaten anyhow. I felt confused and disorientated.

"Am I really stupid?" I wondered, my boundless, naive, faith in myself shattered. "Can it be that I am just plain stupid?"

"Or is the whole world stupid?" And chaotic; and incomprehensible? Everything was so topsy-turvy. On the very first day I had told the truth as I knew it about Africa, and was called a liar. Then I had wanted to read, something I thought was reasonable and perfectly natural, and yet I had been told I was cheeky. I thought I had simply told the truth, been candid and honest with Miss Brown and yet she had called me precocious. The story that I had always believed to be funny was called rude. Now my brown friends, whom I knew, I absolutely knew, to be polite and dignified, were called uncivilised black savages.

Everything, all my old certainties, all my easy, comfortable beliefs were turned upside down, and back to front.

As I stood there, in the middle of the playground, loneliness came slithering up, and engulfed me in its cold, icy embrace, constricting my throat, so that I could hardly breathe, squeezing me, freezing me, into a frozen pillar of ice. The north wind added its icy breath, whipping the dried autumn leaves around my feet, draining the last vestiges of warmth from my body.

Even the other children were feeling the cold. The group sitting in a circle had fetched their coats from their pegs, and the majority, who were playing ball games or chasing games were whipping themselves into a noisy, boisterous frenzy, so that their cheeks were rosy and glowing in spite of the cold.

How I wished I could be part of those games, instead of an isolated island of one. Miss Ashburn had isolated me as effectively as if she had stood me in a corner with a dunce's cap on my head; as effectively as if she had put me inside a barbed wire cage.

As I stood there, in a patch of no-mans-land by myself, I started to imagine that I was surrounded by a fence of cruel barbed wire, worse than the barbed wire fences on the farm, coiled and twisted, riddled with sharp barbs, like those I had seen in war pictures; so that I dared not move to join the other children, nor could any of them come to make friendly overtures to me.

Not that it was likely that even one of them wanted to be friends, the glances that were shot in my direction were barbed; they were sharper, more pointed, more wounding than any barbed wire could be.

"You're a liar," I imagined the barbed, pointed looks saying.

"Cheeky."

"Rude."

"Precocious."

Loneliness, I thought, is something you are meant to feel when you are alone. Yet I had never, ever, felt lonely before, even though I had often been quite, quite alone. Why then now, in the midst of a crowded playground of children?

Lunchtime was only an hour, but to me it seemed an eternity before the bell went and all the children formed themselves into crocodile files holding their partners' hands. I joined the class just as they were leading in, once more the lone figure at the crocodile's tail.

I took the cruel, coiled barbed wire with me into the classroom, because for the whole afternoon no one came near me, or shared any task with me.

After school, when we went out the front door, the two boys jostled me again.

"You're a liar, you've never been to Africa," said one.

"You've learned to be uncivilised from those black savages in Africa," added the other, mimicking the teacher.

"You're both stupid, don't you see, you contradict one another!"

"You're a show-off! You use stupid big words to show off," one of them retorted.

I felt a surge of fury building up again. I would have flown at them, attacking tooth and nail, had Mother's car not drawn up at that moment.

"I'm never going back to that school ever again!" I told her furiously. But my mother took no notice, and merely smiled blandly.

"There, there, you'll soon get used to it," she said.

All that night I dreamt I was in a barbed wire cage. I had turned into one of the proud mountain eagles that soar and glide so effortlessly in the updraught of the mountain winds. But in the dream, I was in a barbed wire cage, so small that I could not stretch my wings, let alone soar over my beloved mountains. And around the cage, poking and pointing and taunting were the leering masks of the teacher and all my classmates.

CHAPTER FOUR

MY MOTHER
AND MY FATHER

"Knowledge comes but wisdom lingers."

TENNYSON

The next morning I was tired and haggard and could not eat breakfast. I repeated my resolution.

"I am not going to school!"

But once more Mother took no notice and said blandly, "You'll soon settle in. Your father will drive you today on his way to the hospital."

I sat in the car seat, feeling very small and helpless. I bunched myself up, in a foetal position, wondering whether I could make myself shrink like Alice in Wonderland. Perhaps, I thought, I can make myself smaller and smaller until I disappear altogether; then they can't make me go to school. But, although I really did feel as though I was getting smaller and smaller, shrinking into the seat, I could not make myself disappear altogether. I was still there when the car stopped outside the school, and even though it was warm inside the car, I felt the icy hands of loneliness creep around me and constrict and squeeze my throat until I could no longer breathe.

Father turned to me, and then he seemed to be opening his bag and taking out his stethoscope and listening to my chest and the next minute he was speeding off home again. He carried me indoors.

"Quick, get her into a warm room and turn on a steam-kettle!" he said to Mother. "She is having an asthma attack. I'll go to the chemist for medication."

The steam, the sedation, the medication, the warmth were soothing and comforting and soon I stopped fighting for breath, snuggled in under the eiderdown and slept. I slept most of that day, and most of the next. The house seemed protective, warm, a shelter against the howling winter winds, and slashing rain and sleet that pounded at the window; a protection against the cruel barbs of the outside world.

In the evenings, because I had slept almost all day, I was allowed to stay up late until Father came home. Until then Father had been almost like a stranger to me, I had so seldom been alone with him.

Now he took me into his study and showed me his encyclopaedias and medical books, and from the back of the cupboard he pulled out an old anatomical model from his student days.

"This is the heart," he said, "and the lungs."

"And there is the liver and behind that the kidneys," I piped in.

"How did you know that?" he asked.

"Oh, I watch, when they butcher the sheep," I replied matter-of-factly. "Boy once showed me the tiny pink deer from inside a pregnant doe too. It was perfect, even more perfect than a newborn kitten."

This had happened recently. My step-grandfather was very protective of the wild game on his property, but once in a while, when he had a visitor, the men would go out on horseback to shoot.

On this occasion he came into the kitchen, and Gran asked mildly, "Did you get some venison?"

"Yes," he said, "but the fool shot a female." He sounded angry and upset; he absolutely forbad the shooting of females. "And at this time of the year she was probably pregnant too."

I shot out of the kitchen to the cool stone room in the outbuilding complex where Boy, the elderly man entrusted with the skinning and butchering of the sheep, worked. The buck carcass had been entrusted to him, and I asked him if he could find the baby inside. Relating the story to my father, I could convey my interest, but not my sense of awe at what I had seen. My father seemed very pleased about my curiosity and my interest in anatomy.

On another occasion, because I talked incessantly about Gran he said, "I, too, had a remarkable grandmother," and he told me about her. She had been an only child, and although she had lived in the middle of the nineteenth century, she had been remarkably independent and liberated; she had travelled extensively, and he told me of some of her adventures, in Venice, and in America at a time when the "wild west" was still untamed.

Then she had married, moved into the house in Highgate, and had four sons.

She still wanted to travel, so to make her passion for travel respectable, to give her an excuse to move around Europe and America, she deposited her sons at schools around the world.

"The eldest, my Uncle David, in Paris, to the Sorbonne to study Medicine. Her second son she sent to New York where he could absorb the American trait of business acumen; he is the father of our American and Canadian cousins. My own father, James, came next, and because he showed a flair for languages he was sent, first to Switzerland, to brush up on his French and Italian, then to Heidelberg for German, even to Latvia for a little while to add the Balkan languages to his bag. The fourth son, Ernest, went to Flanders where he could study art with an eminent Flemish painter."

I showed an interest at this. "An artist?"

"Yes, Ernest became a reasonably successful portrait painter in London; but both his sons are doctors," the last phrase very, very emphatically, almost as though a slight aberration in the family had quickly reverted to the norm. Every one of my father's own brothers, and even his sister, had studied either medicine or science. There seemed to be no wayward artists in HIS generation.

Unlike Gran's fairytales, and my little brown friends' stories, which were highly fanciful, my father's stories were about real people, or more often, about real facts, mostly scientific facts, but he had a flair for finding factual information fascinating, and transmitting his enthusiasm. I thought he knew so much; and like a sponge, I tried to absorb every word he said.

So I enjoyed that first week at home, finding the evenings with my father far more interesting than school, even though Mother would occasionally walk in and say to him,

"You know, you are talking far above the child's head."

One day when I awoke, I could no longer hear the howling wind and slashing rain. I felt an urgent need to get out into the open.

"Mother, can we go outside for a walk?" I asked.

"Don't be silly," said Mother, "Not in this smog."

I ran to the window and pulled the curtains aside. Outside was a dense, dense smog; so dense that I could not see a thing – not even the tree that grew near the house. It was like nothing I had ever seen before.

Nothing at all like the white mist that once in a while rolled down from the mountains and enveloped the farmhouse. That was snowy white, white as a cloud, as if a cloud had become tired of floating in the sky and had settled down on the mountainside for a rest. That mist only lasted a little while, early in the morning, and then as the sun warmed, it turned wispy and swirly so that the landscape looked like a water-colour painting. I loved the way that mist transformed the hard outlines of the mountains into blurred shadowy images, made the solid granite cliffs and krantzes seem to float weightlessly in the sky. Then before long the mist would dissolve away leaving a bright, still sunny day.

This smog was quite different. Not snowy white, but dingy, dirty grey, an acidic yellowish, greenish grey, and it showed no sign of dissipating. I shuddered. All day I ran from window to window in the house, and all day the fog pressed and pushed against the glass. The house that had seemed a warm, comforting shelter, seemed to change and become a trap; a cage, a prison. It seemed to press in on me, dark, forbidding, eerie, joining forces with the smog to keep me from the sun and the sky.

I longed desperately for the sky, for the huge azure dome hanging high high above the mountains, not the little low glimpses of grey between the buildings that was all I seemed to see in London. I pined for my mighty, majestic mountains and that vast sense of space.

That night, I dreamed again that I was a mountain eagle but this time instead of being in a barbed wire cage, I was covered in a heavy, wet blanket. A dingy, khaki-grey blanket, exactly the colour of the smog. It was cold and wet and clammy, and so, so heavy.

All night I struggled to spread my wings, to fly up to the sky, but the blanket pressed down so heavily, clung so clammily that I could not even spread my wings, let alone fly. I tried to lift my head to take a deep breath to renew the struggle, and instead of fresh mountain air my throat and lungs were choked with the cold, clammy smog. More and more desperately I struggled until the sleek, shiny wings were broken and bedraggled, until there was no longer any hope of ever flying again.

I woke up, frightened and exhausted. I ran to the window, pulled back the curtain, and there it was still, thick and turgid, pressing itself against the glass. The house seemed to have shrunk, pressing in on all sides, threatening to crush me; dark, cold, claustrophobic. Panic-stricken and desperate I went to find mother.

"Mother, please, please, let me go back to Gran," I pleaded. To my horror, Mother's face turned bleak and forlorn and her eyes brimmed with tears.

"How cruel it is," she sighed, "when one's only child prefers to live with someone else."

A tear trickled down her cheek.

I was nonplussed. I had been so wrapped up in my own distress that I had forgotten how sensitive Mother was, how easily hurt. I had been prepared to argue and plead my case; even throw a little tantrum if necessary, but my mother's tears stopped me in my tracks.

It is almost impossible to stand up to my mother; she makes me feel so guilty when I am self-willed, and she is so beautiful, with her thick, wavy hair, all different shades of gold and amber and copper. Whenever I think of my mother's warm colouring I think of a necklace she sometimes wears, a necklace of huge amber beads that exactly pick up the golds and ambers in her hair, and the rich amber flecks in her hazel eyes, warm beads that seem to caress the warm gold of her skin.

She once told me that that necklace had been an heirloom, not of our family, but another family. They had lent it to her to go to a ball, because it went so well with her copper lamé ballgown. Then, when they saw it on her, they exclaimed how perfectly beautifully it went with her gold and amber hair, her eyes and her golden complexion, and insisted that she keep it. It did not suit their own daughter's pink skin. Of course I know that necklace will never be passed on to me, my mother will say that the colours are far too rich for my pale colouring.

My mother wears all my favourite colours, golds and bronzes; russets and rusts and ambers and clarets; all the warm colours of autumn, all the rich comforting terracotta reds of the earth itself. She dresses me in white. Or sometimes navy blue, or pale, washed-out green.

Seeing the tears, brimming on the edge of my mother's bottom eyelids, I did not have the heart to persist about going back to Africa, but I was still desperately reluctant to go back to Miss Pinkerton's, so I said meekly, "Then please don't send me to school."

"But of course you must go to school; you know how important education is to your father."

So, when the week at home was over, and the smog had cleared a little, I was sent back to school.

School was even worse than the claustrophobic house. The boys still taunted and teased me and enjoyed my spirited reaction. Miss Ashburn still lashed at me with her sarcastic and acid tongue.

I felt lonely, icy cold, isolated. Three days later I had another asthma attack.

So the weeks went by, some days I was sent to school, which meant I was sent to bed early before my father came home, on others I was imprisoned in the house all day, fighting to breathe. Neither was less miserable than the other.

Then one day Mother said. "I have some news for you. Your grandfather is coming to London on some business. He'll be able to give you news of your friends. That should cheer you up."

It did just the opposite. My grandfather was cheerful enough; and gave me all the news.

"Your grandmother was like a cat without a tail after you left," he said. "And as for Ethel and Iris! They sat in the kitchen and wailed for a week."

How I missed my old, comfortable friends. He told all the good news. "Dinah's sister had a baby, a boy. At least that distracted Iris and Ethel."

I wished that I too could see the new brown baby.

"Your cat had another litter of kittens. All tiger-striped just like their mother."

I missed my cat so, missed that tactile, caressing relationship, and I longed to cuddle the tiny kittens, and laugh at their funny antics. They would not let me have a cat in London.

"There's some sad news too. John was riding Fonk along the road, galloping hard, when he was startled by a dassie, so he veered off the road, and caught his hoof in the dassie hole and fell. Broke a leg. There was nothing we could do. Had to shoot him."

I felt sad, terribly sad, for John, because I knew how much he loved his fine white horse, but I felt as though I had known all along that the beautiful horse would not live long, and the news only added to my homesickness. The more Grandfather talked, about the lambing, and the shearing, and about the new borehole in the far paddock, that produced so much water that he was going to plant some willow trees around it; the more I longed to be part of that far-off, familiar world.

When the meal was over I was sent to bed, but I lay there for hours unable to sleep. Suddenly I jumped up, ran around my bedroom, collecting books, and odds and ends into a basket. Carrying it carefully, I tip-toed down to Father's study. There was still a chink of light showing under the door. I tapped and walked in.

"Father," I said quickly. "You believe a good education is important don't you?"

Father raised his eyebrows but did not say anything so I went on even more quickly and breathlessly.

"Well, to get a good education you need a good teacher. And Gran is the best. Much better than those stupid teachers at school."

His eyebrows shot up even higher. But there was no stopping me now. "Look," I said. "Look at this big book Gran taught me to read, and this book of poems. I'll read you some." I opened first the big book, and then the small book of poetry that I had partially memorised, and read quickly, breathlessly.

"See!" I exclaimed, "and at school Miss Ashburn says we are not ready to read. And in Miss Brown's class all they read is the cat sat on the mat. And," I said, racing on, stringing my sentences together, not pausing to take a breath, determined to get it in before Father interrupted – although if I stopped to think about it, he had not yet said a single word; "and," I continued, "Miss Ashburn makes us string big, wooden beads all day. It's so silly. Look what I made. Dinah helped me, but I made most of it." And I proffered a bracelet of intricately woven chevron patterns, made of tiny, tiny glass beads in green, black, yellow and white.

"And I learnt so many other things. I know all the flowers and Grandpa was teaching me the stars, and you can't even see stars here." I had quite run out of breath.

"Can I go back with him?" I finished, gasping for breath.

Father spoke at last.

"We'll see, we'll see."

My spirits sank. I knew what "We'll see" meant. It was something that grown-ups said when they meant "no" but did not have the courage to say it outright to your face.

I dragged myself back to bed.

The next day I was apathetic and dispirited. When the boys teased me at school, they did not get any response; when Miss Ashburn told me to string beads, I meekly obeyed.

Just before lunch, I was sitting near the doorway apathetically stringing beads when I heard Miss Pinkerton talking to a man in the hallway. Suddenly I lifted my head and sniffed. I was sure I could smell the faintest whiff of chloroform. When my father had been in surgery all day, he also had that faintest smell of anaesthetic about him.

Then suddenly, there was my father; walking towards Miss Ashburn, escorted by Miss Pinkerton, who was fussing and clucking like a scrawny old hen.

He greeted Miss Ashburn heartily and then said, "Now carry on, carry on teaching."

Miss Ashburn continued to stand there, mutely wringing her hands.

"Please, please my dear Miss Ashburn, continue to impart your pearls of wisdom to your pupils."

He bestowed upon her his most brilliant smile; a smile of blatant charm that quite flustered Miss Ashburn.

"Ignore me! Just pretend I am not here."

I could not help smiling to myself. My father is a big man, over six feet tall, and exudes the kind of presence that is impossible to ignore. Miss Ashburn certainly could not.

"Well then," he said at last, "if you will not teach, perhaps you will show me your programme, or curriculum or syllabus or whatever the jargon is for your aims and intentions for the pupils this year."

Miss Ashburn took out a folder and my father flicked through it.

"That will be all," he said and started towards the door, with Miss Ashburn following behind, almost herding him out. In the doorway he stopped and turned.

"Why are those children stringing beads?"

At long last Miss Ashburn found her tongue. "Oh," she said, "that is very good for their motor development. It gives them fine hand-eye co-ordination." She seemed pleased with her own explanation.

Father put his hand in his pocket and drew out my bracelet. He proffered it to Miss Ashburn, but she only stared at it as if it were a snake that could bite her.

"You call that motor co-ordination?" he smiled brilliantly.

"Now this," he revolved the fine beadwork slowly in his hand, almost under her nose. "Now this, I would say, required fine motor co-ordination."

I could not be sure but it seemed Father winked at me, before he turned to go. I heard him go, briefly, with Miss Pinkerton, into Miss Brown's classroom, and then soon afterwards out the big front door.

It all happened so quickly, it was all so strange. Perhaps I had just dreamt it. Then I remembered the chloroform smell. "You can't dream smells," I told myself.

That evening Father came home in time for dinner, which was most unusual. While we were sipping our soup my grandfather asked my father about some battle in the war.

At first my father seemed distracted and answered absentmindedly, but then his enthusiasm returned, and he picked up the cruet set, "This is El Alamein," he said positioning the salt cellar, "and here is Tobruk," pointing to the pepper shaker; then he leaned back behind him, to pull the chess trolley to the table. He spread the chessmen haphazardly around the pristine white tablecloth; the black king he called Rommel and the rest of the blacks he called "Gerry," then the white king was Monty and his men had names like "the eighth army," or "the allies."

Talking about out-flanking and out-manoevring, about retreating and counter-attacking, he moved the chess pieces around. Sometimes a white piece defeated a black piece, and then the latter was returned to the chess board.

Once the black knight took the white knight, and my mother spoke, and in her voice I recognised the tension that had been in her voice on the farm, in the war, when she had listened to the B.B.C. "I thought that you were there. I thought you were with them. I was sure you had been taken prisoner!"

"Oh no," said my father casually, not recognising the tension, because he had not heard it before the way I had, "No, by that time I was here, with this crowd," and he pointed to the white castle.

By the time we had finished our soup, the game was over. My father had made war sound so strategic, so civilised, almost like a game of chess.

During the main course, my grandfather asked, "Did you have a gun?"

And my father said, "Yes, a revolver."

"Did you have to use it?" I felt my mother's tension transfer to me, as I waited to hear whether my father had had to shoot a Gerry.

"No," he said. "No never," and I relaxed again.

Then it seemed my father's turn to be tense, to seem to start to say something, only to fall silent again.

At last, when Mother brought in the dessert, he said, suddenly, firmly, "We have a very important decision to make that concerns all four of us."

He paused, and then went on. "Last night I was visited in my study, with the proposition that Gran was a better teacher than Miss Pinkerton's staff." He stopped and smiled disarmingly. My father, when he is earnest, sometimes has this way of speaking rather pompously, and then smiling in an almost self-deprecating way, as if to invite others to challenge his statement; but nobody spoke.

"Unexpectedly, I find myself concurring," he continued. "I paid the school a visit today. Gran's teaching might be unorthodox but she has a deep and abiding love of literature and poetry, and an adventurous and enthusiastic sense of enquiry, and that is often the best teacher."

I had been looking down at my plate while he spoke, stirring the little sea of custard around and around the island of steamed pudding. My father and grandfather were at the ends of the table so I sat in the middle, directly opposite Mother.

Slowly I lifted my eyes, dreading the sight of Mother's face, dreading the hurt, injured look I was sure to see, remembering the brimming eyes last time I suggested going back to Gran.

My eyes moved slowly across the table and then stopped at the sight of my mother's hands. Mother had put down her spoon and pushed her plate aside. She had taken up the silver serviette ring and was turning and twisting it in her hands. How those hands agonised and twisted and writhed. My mother's fine, delicate, soft, usually serene hands were tortured, agonising. I watched them, transfixed. I could not wrench my gaze from those hands.

Father continued his monologue.

"Then again, a far more pressing concern is her health. I had a cousin who was a chronic asthmatic. He died young." For the first time in my life, I heard Father's voice tremble.

"I could not impose that sort of life or death on a child, knowing that in another place she could be fit and healthy."

Still, the fine white hands twisted and writhed. The face which I could not bring myself to look up to, must have been just as agonised, because Father continued soothingly, coaxingly.

"Don't you see, my dear, her health and happiness are both at stake? It would only be for a year or two. In two years I'll no longer be tied to the London hospital, if she still reacts to this climate, we'll move somewhere warmer and drier, America, Australia, Africa, wherever you like."

Still there was silence. The hands laid down the silver napkin ring and disappeared down under the tablecloth.

Not a word came from opposite the table but Mother must have nodded because suddenly Grandfather was saying loudly and heartily, "Wonderful! Wonderful! Gran will be in her seventh heaven! And the fresh mountain air and fresh farm food will soon put the roses back into those pale cheeks."

CHAPTER FIVE

"CHILD OF THE MOUNTAINS"

"I cry Love! Love! Happy happy love!
Free as the mountain wind."

WILLIAM BLAKE

I could not wait for the first glimpse of my beloved mountains, but it was a long journey, by ship and by train and by car, so that by the time the dark mountains finally loomed into view, I was fast asleep, curled up like a kitten, on the back seat of the car. I was carried, still sleeping, into bed.

The first glimmer of dawn was a bare sliver of silver-grey in the gap between the curtains when I awoke.

For a moment I wondered where I was; why I no longer felt the rocking ship or rattling train under me. Then, with a yelp of delight, I leapt up out of bed.

"I'm home!"

Then I wondered, "Have I woken in time?"

I ran to my old chest of drawers, pulled out an old pair of grey flannel dungarees and a woollen jersey and hastily dragged them on. Then, clutching my shoes in my hands I raced up the long corridor towards the kitchen. All the bedrooms led off this corridor, most with the doors ajar so that I could hear the sleepers steadily breathing or snoring but, as yet, no one was stirring. The door from the corridor to the kitchen was locked, but the big key was on my side, so I unlocked it and slipped through.

The kitchen was warmer than the rest of the house, the iron stove just barely alight. The last one to go to bed filled it with shovelfuls of coal, and closed down the damper so that it barely glowed through the night. The next morning all Dinah had to do was open up the damper to let air in, and it would burst back into flame so that she could make early morning coffee for everyone. A special alcove had been built in behind the stove to keep orphaned lambs overnight until they were old enough to survive in a pen in the wool shed. I was in too much of a hurry to check if there were any lambs there now.

Out the unlocked back door I went, across the swept gravel yard, past the outbuildings and up the steep foothill behind the house. I was running now and stumbling, cracking my shins on the jagged rocks because, although the sky was slowly lightening, the ground was still black as night.

At last I reached the top of the hill. I looked to the east, and although the sky was perceptibly lighter, a pale, pearly grey, there was no sign of the sun.

"I am in time!" I sighed with relief.

Then I looked to the west, to the huge, towering mountains, two dimensional, steel blue, against a grey blue sky. I kept staring at them, not daring to glance away for a split second.

Then it happened! The topmost peak burst into flame – a brilliant, glowing, golden orange beacon against the blue grey, steel grey world. I glanced back to the east and still could not see the sun.

West again, and now the whole spiny crest of the range glowed with molten gold, a jewelled necklace against the steel grey sky.

This time when I looked east the sun was just heaving itself over the lower mountain ranges, and now I myself, and the rocks I was standing on, were bathed in golden light, while the farmhouse and valleys below were still dark, misty, shadowy. Only the tips of the dense grove of pine trees, which gave the farm its name, "The Pines" were brushed with light.

Then, having heaved himself up, the sun seemed to gather strength and raise himself into the sky at ever increasing speed, dispelling the mists and shadows, until soon the whole world stretched around me, bathed in soft morning light.

Oh how I ached with the sheer joy, the exhilaration, the wonder, the ecstasy I felt as I witnessed the birth of a new day!

Then, just as moving, in a different way, I remembered the sweet sad dimming of the landscape as the day died. In towns and suburbs with electricity, where artificial lights immediately replace the sun, there is so little sense of this cycle of the days' birth and death, one never feels as intensely that welling exhilaration as the sun rises, the feeling of one's spirit rising with the sun, that expectation of something magical and miraculous about to happen. And in those days every day seemed an unfolding revelation, until the sun slipped suddenly behind the mountains to the west, and we would be steeped in hauntingly sad, yearning wistfulness as another day died.

Ecstatically, I stretched out my arms and circled around and around.

It was all exactly as I remembered it. Every rock, every mountain, every tree, every windmill, exactly where it should be. All so pristine new in the new day, yet so achingly old and familiar.

I lifted my head, still circling around and around, and saw the mountain eagle spiralling upwards into the glowing vault of heaven, greeting the sun with his shrill cries.

Then, just before he merged into the brilliance of the sun, he swooped and banked, and showed me his back, and there, emblazoned on his black back, in pure white, was the exact mirror image of the shape I felt I made, standing there with my arms forming great arcs above my head. He is taking my gladness to share it with the sun, I thought joyfully, and I found myself whooping and singing a response to his cries.

"We are free! And everything is perfect!" I responded, again and again to his shrill call.

At last I looked down again, at the circle of circular thatched roofed huts, throwing long, black, triangular shadows against the hillside, and as I looked I saw three figures starting down the path towards the farmhouse.

Then I was running, leaping downhill, agile as a mountain goat, now that I could see the rocks in high relief side-lit by the sun. Down to the path, worn into a deep rut, racing along it, still singing, shouting, whooping, "*Jonga Kum!*" Look at me! Look at me!

"*Ndibuyile!*" I am back!

Look at me! I am back! until I came to a sudden panting halt in front of Dinah and Ethel and Iris.

"We see you," said Ethel solemnly.

"You are back," said Iris gravely.

I was momentarily stunned by the reserve of their welcome. Then Dinah stretched open her arms, "It is good that you are back!"

I flung myself at Dinah's ample bosom. I smelled her pungent odour, so different from Mother's rose and lavender perfume, and I rubbed my cheek against the coarse red blanket that Dinah had over her shoulders in the early morning chill, the same rough, coarsely woven blanket she had used to strap me on to her back; so different from my mother's silky, soft dresses.

I echoed, "It is good that I am back."

"This is where you belong," said Dinah.

"This is where I belong," I repeated.

"Here with you and Ethel and Iris and the mountains."

I jumped up and lifted up my arms.

"Look at the mountains! My wonderful, wonderful mountains!" I cried rapturously, "They are just so..." and I stopped, lost for the right word. I had been talking in their language right from the very first "look at me". After all one does not greet a person with such a phrase in English! Yet I was surprised how clumsy my tongue felt making the difficult clicking sounds of some of the words; my tongue grows lazy very easily, and loses its suppleness, like a gymnast who does not exercise for a few months.

Also, I was thinking in English, and the phrase that came to mind, in English, was "majestic mountains". So I translated it, clumsily, the best way I could, back into their language.

"Aren't those mountains so-like-a-king?"

Dinah burst into laughter. Her whole voluptuous body shook and heaved with laughter.

"Haw, aren't you a funny one, my little Child of the Mountains! *Mntwana Wasezintabeni!*" she laughed and laughed, and I had to laugh at myself, and at my own silly, clumsy expression, and in sheer delight at the new name that Dinah had given me.

"Child of the Mountains," I echoed. "I am a Child of the Mountains!"

Then Ethel and Iris shed their initial reserve and shyness and laughed and giggled too; and so we went, all four of us, laughing and giggling down the path to the house.

Later that afternoon, I went back to the kraal to visit some of my old friends. The houses were all alike; circular or rondavel-shaped, cylinders of mud wall with no windows at all and only one door, topped with a roof of thatch. Inside the floors were a mixture of the same red anthill clay as the tennis court, but here dung was added, smeared on when still moist and fresh so that it dried hard and shiny. Although most of the cooking was done over outdoor fires, in winter some embers were taken indoors for warmth, so that over the years the interior became smoke-darkened, and even in summer smelled of thorn-wood smoke.

As I arrived at the circle of huts the first person I saw was a very wizened old man with grey hair and beard, sitting beside the doorway of his home, smoking a pipe.

I went up to him holding out my hand and said, "I see you, Old Grandfather." He grasped my hand.

"I see you, Child of the Mountains," he replied solemnly.

I was thrilled, and surprisingly, not at all surprised that he had used exactly the same name for me as Dinah had used that morning, though in the past he had called me, in his own language, "The little *N'kosi* with the white head."

I loved my new name. I now thought of myself, always as "Child of the Mountains".

Soon, as if by some telepathic agreement, every one of the natives was calling me "Child of the Mountains".

Everyone, that is, except Ethel and Iris. They called me by my

English name, and they liked me to use their English names. Now this DID surprise me! Especially as neither girl would speak a word of English.

I often tried to persuade them to.

"Go on," I would say. "Just say 'Good morning. It's a lovely day'," but the girls would put their hands over their mouths, and giggle nervously. I knew if I persisted, that they would be overcome with shyness and embarrassment. So I would drop the subject, even though I knew that they understood me perfectly when I spoke, because now and then I would give them an instruction in English, and they would always do exactly as I said.

As the months went by, I took to reading to them. My own reading had come along in leaps and bounds, and Gran had only to read me a story, going back to repeat the longer, or more difficult words once or twice; then I could read the whole story to Ethel and Iris.

I wanted to share this fascination with Ethel and Iris. I wanted to teach them to read, but if they would not speak English, how could I make them read it? So I went to Gran.

"Are there books in Xhosa?" I asked.

"I'm sure there must be," said Gran. "Though how the European alphabet copes with the dialect they speak up here, where many words are mere clicks of the tongue, I really don't know."

So I went back to my friends,

"If I can get a book in your language, would you like to learn to read?"

Ethel and Iris were very fond of me, and they knew that this strange ritual of reading meant a great deal to me. They were also by nature very circumspect, and very tactful. So the conversation that followed was very, very long, very involved, now one speaking, then the other, with much beating around the bush, much hinting, innuendo and suggesting.

The gist of the matter was, however, that Ethel and Iris thought that people who needed to look at black signs on a piece of paper in order to tell a story, must be stupid.

Intelligent people kept stories in their heads. A really clever person remembered every story ever told to them from tales told at their grandmother's knee to the latest offerings of the itinerant storytellers.

Some stories, like the traditional folklore of the tribe had to be remembered and memorised exactly, while other stories were only starting points and a storyteller could embroider, enlarge, add a sequel, or even invent out of their heads, completely new stories. They reminded me gently that the wise Old Grandfather did not find it necessary to read to be profoundly wise, the wise witchdoctor lady did not need to read to cure all kinds of ills, their mother and their father did not read.

They were so circumspect about their rejection of my idea that I had to accept their refusal graciously, but I was bitterly disappointed. I loved reading so much, and I still believed pleasures were greater when shared. I was also keen to see their language written down, turned into signs, sensing that I would be more likely to remember it forever if I had seen it as well as heard it. Even then I sensed that I had not inherited an ear for languages from my father, and grandfather, the one who was educated in Switzerland and Heidelberg and Latvia, picking up languages as easily as bouquets of flowers.

Once Gran stopped reading aloud to me, once I graduated to teaching myself, I began to see some words, not as sounds, but as symbols and signals, instantly in a split-second flash sparking their meaning to me. Soon I had a whole host of words that were old friends, I knew them intimately, every nuance of their moods, but I could not introduce them into a conversation because I had no idea how to say them. Take a simple word like ubiquitous. Was the first letter pronounced "yoo", or as in umbrella? I seemed to register names and words as pure symbols, like Egyptian hieroglyphics or Chinese characters.

This lopsided bias towards the written symbol, towards meaning rather than sound, did not inhibit a love for the sensuality of language, nor did it prevent my deliberately delighting in an eclectic mixture of languages. Long after Landi left I was still sprinkling sentences with the little smattering of Italian words that he had taught me.

Of course there were also times when I completely muddled words and languages. One of the silliest was when I was very young, when we still had the two Italian prisoners, and they were having dinner with the family, instead of being served in their quarters. In fact they had cooked the meal! All afternoon they had worked away in Dinah's kitchen, while she hovered around, complaining to me in her language, that it was not right that men should cook, that there should not be men in her kitchen, and what they were doing was downright ridiculous. She kept up a continuous denigrating commentary, so that I was thankful they could not understand a word of her tongue-clicking criticism.

They made a mound of flour with an indent in the middle on the scrubbed wooden table, and then broke several eggs into the middle, making a thick, sticky dough, which they rolled out wafer-thin and cut into strips which they hung up to dry, like socks on a washline. Then we went out into the vegetable garden and picked great baskets of tomatoes, and pulled out small onions, and cut bunches of herbs, chives and oregano and red peppers and chillis. They called the dish they made "pasta".

Gran still served the meal. When it came to second helpings the other man nodded and said, "*Grazie.*"

But Landi said, "*Grazie, grazie,* but no, I have had sufficient."

"You have had enough?" repeated Gran.

Then I piped up in a loud voice, "Sufficient means enough in

Italian!" I was very small at the time, and I think I had been show-ing off, with the few Italian words that Landi had taught me. They all laughed at me, even the Italians.

"No silly, sufficient is an English word. You probably never heard it used before," said Kay.

I still remember being inordinately embarrassed. Perhaps it was my acute embarrassment that makes me remember the incident. Then the embarrassment turned to a sort of defiance; why should I not mix and muddle languages, collect words that I liked, words that were per-fect for the job and lost their punch in translation, even if other people ridiculed me?

After all my mother quite naturally used French words like *"faux pas"* in English sentences, and my father often used Latin words like *"a priori"*.

In England I had realised how many words I used were foreign to my classmates, that I was actually mixing Zulu words and Xhosa words and Afrikaans words in with my English. For instance I had used the word, *"donga"*.

"What's that?" asked a little boy. So I explained that it was a deep ravine-like river with no water in it. He thought I was mad!

It is a Zulu word that perfectly describes the deeply eroded fis-sures and gorges that the sudden African storms gouge deep into the red clay soil below the steep mountains. Farmers hate them, because they are synonymous with soil erosion, but I thought they made marvel-lous branching patterns on the landscape. There is no word for them in English, because most English rivers behave differently, gently mean-dering, full of water, flowing between green hills.

The same applies to the Dutch *plaas jaapie*. It is a wonderful phrase full of layers of meaning, absolutely impossible to translate. An idiomatic dictionary might suggest "farm yokel", or "country bumpkin", but those approximations would fail to convey the real essence of that phrase, an essence of wide-eyed, wondering, childlike innocence and naive faith. Most of all a belief, a conviction, that everyone else is straight down the line; a sanguine, vulnerable, dumb belief in the innate goodness of human nature.

Farmers used it to poke fun at themselves, at the mercy of sophisticated city slickers, but it is also a perfect description of the way I was.

Over the months I reconciled myself to the fact that reading could not be a shared pleasure, that it was something I did quite alone; that there were a few things that I would have to explore alone. Painting was another one.

For Christmas that year I was sent a magnificent paintbox and, rather incongruously with it, one of those colouring-in books with big, simple pictures in even black outlines.

Now I had never painted before, not even at school, where they only had crayons. I had never seen anyone paint either. Most things one learns by imitating someone else. Even making clay oxen was something I had learned from my friends, who had learned from their older friends. But in painting I had no role model, no guide, and, probably best of all, no other children to remark on my efforts. Sometimes there is a wonderfully liberating freedom about isolation!

There were twelve palettes of colours, beautiful colours, with colourful names like viridian, vermilion, ultramarine, printed on tracing paper over the cubes.

The first picture in the colouring-in book was a rabbit. I painted the top of his ear alizarin crimson, then a cobalt stripe, then some naples yellow. Part of his body I divided up into curving shapes like a jig-saw puzzle, each piece a different colour, until I had tried every one of the twelve colours. Then I started mixing colours, sometimes making brilliant new colours, sometimes muddy greys! At one stage I arranged seven strips of colour in the same order as the rainbow, along the arch of the rabbit's back.

John walked past at that moment and glanced at what I was doing,

"That is a rabbit," he said. "Rabbits are supposed to be brown," in the patient, monotone, know-all tone he sometimes used.

I spun around indignantly. John had lost his godlike infallibility for me, ever since he had told me that schools taught one to read.

"This is NOT a rabbit. Rabbits are warm, furry and hop along the ground."

He laughed, and walked on.

Suddenly I took up the paintbrush and inserted a big NOT into the caption, so that it became, "This is NOT a rabbit," and then I went and showed it to Gran.

She exclaimed at my lovely colours, at the seven colours of the rainbow all in the right order, "Red, orange, yellow, green, blue, indigo, violet," she recited, but she made no comment at all about the caption, and suddenly a terrible thought occurred to me.

"Perhaps she does not understand. This cannot be. My Gran always understands everything. Why not now?"

This is the very first time I remember this happening to me, though it has happened many, many times since.

Something was quite obvious, but nobody else understood!

Now, for almost all of the time, for almost all of my life, I am vexed and puzzled by my own painful lack of understanding. I try to work things out, but most of the time, I am completely dumb; so many things are a mysterious enigma to me. Yet, once in a while I see something, see it in a clear white blinding light, and I want to share it, test it against someone else's understanding, but most people think I am stark, staring crazy, or else too big for my boots, if I try to share some wondrous thought.

"This is not a rabbit" might seem unimportant, and perhaps it is, compared with some of the strange and complex things that have been revealed to me lately in my clear blinding light.

It IS very simple, but then, when I was only seven years old, it was a revelation.

It meant that I was free to paint whatever I felt compelled to paint. No matter what I did on a piece of paper, it would never BE a rabbit; even if I painted it very realistically, and brown, it would never be warm, furry and hop. So the painting was a thing in itself, a reality of its own, and I was absolutely free to make it either realistic or a rainbow-jigsaw-kaleidoscope of colour!

This seemed to me to apply even more to three-dimensional forms like my clay oxen. I could change their shape, exaggerate their horns, ignore the conventions of my friends; become engrossed in the sheer beauty of planes and curves; because a clay ox, is a clay ox, a reality in itself; it can never BE an ox, only embody the oxiness of oxen.

In one of those tiny echoes of echoes that echo through my life, the other day, years and years after I painted my rainbow-jigsaw-kaleidoscope rabbit, I was delving into a book and I found a painting, "Ceci n'est pas une pipe".

Books are like treasure chests. As I open the cover of a new book, I imagine that I am lifting the lid of a treasure chest, and wonder what trinket of knowledge, what gem of a new word, or even, occasionally, what pearl of wisdom I will discover. ("Pearl of wisdom" has been one of my favourite clichés ever since my father flustered Miss Ashburn!)

Sometimes one can delve into a book, and find what one is searching for, even when one is not aware of what one is looking for! Most certainly I had not the remotest idea whatsoever that I was looking for a picture of a pipe until I found it, and then I realised that I had, in a sort of way, been looking for it since the day I wrote "This is NOT a rabbit" all those years ago.

A Belgian artist painted a very realistic brown pipe, and underneath it he wrote, on the canvas itself, *"Ceci n'est pas une pipe."** (Belgians must speak French.)

"Of course it is a pipe," would be the predictable first reaction of very nearly everyone who saw it; or everyone who had been brought up with school primers which said, "This is a cat," or "This is a boy," or colouring-in books that said, "This is a rabbit."

Of course the artist's caption, "This is Not a Pipe" is closer to the real truth, and all those captions we are force-fed as children are not truly true at all. No matter how realistically the pipe is portrayed, it is still only oil paint on canvas, a painting, and no one can hold it, light it, and for a pipe to be a pipe one has to be able to smoke it; that is the very essence of pipeness. The book said how clever of Monsieur Rene Magritte to point this out.

I thought, how clever of him to have people listen to him. Nobody, even now, would say how clever if I were to point out that the essence of rabbitness is to be warm, and furry and hop. I wondered again whether so many of the things we are told "are so," or "are true" might not necessarily be true at all, whether all my yearnings to uncover the truth might reveal only shadows.

There was something else interesting about the story of Rene Magritte. Not only did one of his paintings echo my questioning of reality, but another painting confirmed my feelings about imprinting. Rene's mother committed suicide when he was a boy, by jumping off a bridge.

* To view image, go to Google images: Magritte Ceci n'est pas une pipe.

When they fished her body out of the canal she seemed naked because her nightdress had been pushed up and was wrapped around her head. The little boy was so imprinted with this image, that, as a man, in many of his paintings, the faces, even the faces of lovers, were swathed in drapery.

So although I spent most of my days with Ethel and Iris, and the others, climbing mountains, I also liked to be alone sometimes, to paint, and to ponder the kind of things you can only wonder about when you are alone for a while. Even now, all these years later, I still like to ponder the thoughts that had their genesis in those days; and there are times when I wonder if I was not a great deal wiser then, than I am now.

Not smart, nor sophisticated, nor worldly-wise; more the wisdom of wonder, of oneness with the world.

Chapter Six

The Secret Sculptures

"Beauty is truth, truth beauty – that is all

you know on earth, and all you need to know."

John Keats

There was something else I did secretly, alone.

Not far from the house there was a densely planted forest of trees, a dark grove of foreign trees, pines and cypresses, tall and funereal; a taboo island of darkness, strange and incongruous against the warm sunlit landscape. So close together were the pines planted that from the outside the plantation looked impenetrable, closed, dark and forboding, and the barbed wire around it, which seemed to add to the atmosphere of unwelcoming melancholy, was enough for a long time to keep me from even contemplating exploring the forest.

Yet one day, when I was alone, when Ethel and Iris had gone home with their mother, for no rhyme or reason I found myself wandering in the direction of the grove of trees, drawn towards the darkness, mesmerised by the menacing shadow-world.

I had to squeeze, gingerly, through the tightly tensioned, prickly barbed wire fence, pricking my back and gouging my calf, to get into the unaccustomed green gloom under the trees, where it seemed as though different birds with different voices called, and where the wind made a different keening noise through those needles and cones to the way it whistled around the house, or up on the mountains.

I had to weave my way, squeeze my way through the close-ranked guardians, and strain my eyes to see through the pressing gloom.

Then just when my eyes were becoming accustomed to the shadowy darkness I stumbled suddenly into a circle of light, an ethereal limpid green light deflected by the grey-green trees behind me, absorbed and diffused by the black-green trees in front of me.

The oblique sunlight did not reach the ground, nor me, nor the three tall plinths inside the perfectly circular clearing, yet far above glistened a white figure in a radiantly glowing halo of shafting sunlight, blindingly beautiful against the shadowy spires of the cypress pines. The two other plinths were surmounted by huge black granite urns.

I stood there, in this strangely secret sanctuary, dwarfed by the sculptures, transfixed, a small frozen statue myself, captivated by that radiant figure, against the dark viridian-green trees.

At first I thought of it as an angel, but then realised that it could not be an angel, because it had no wings, and angels always had wings. This looked more like a young girl, a very young girl, striding into the wind, her cloak whipped against her body in the front, and billowing behind her, making surging concave and convex shapes. She had gathered a bunch of flowers, and from her lofty plinth was gaily scattering them onto the tombstone way, way below.

Her face was the most sweetly, serenely, exquisitely beautiful face I had ever seen. Not the kind of sentimental sweetness, or pretty beauty, one might imagine from the words sweet and beautiful, but an uplifting and moving, rarified kind of beauty.

I spent a whole afternoon, the first time I ventured there, captivated, with my face uplifted, drinking in that beauty, marvelling at the way it moved me, until it began to fade in the fading light, to turn dim and ghostly and wistfully sad, against the dull red dusk, and the whole world seemed suffused with the all-pervasive, infinite sadness that I always felt as the dying day slipped away, and I felt a kind of yearning ache that I did not understand.

I ran back under trees turned tall, black, crowding together, threatening to herd me back to that inner space, menacing, a phalanx of grim guardians. It seemed I would never break through their ranks, through the thickets of needles turned sharp and prickly, like barbed wire, but then all at once it was the black, barbed-wire fence itself that I found myself caught up in. I clambered through it, and then out into the purple-red gloom of the gathering dusk.

As I rushed, panic-stricken, into the reassuring familiarity of the garden, my aunt, Kay, caught me.

"I have been searching for you," she scolded. "You haven't been to the graves, have you?"

"Is that what they are!" I replied excitedly, then I had to ask, "What are they? Why are they there?"

"Your grandfather, and his brother, and your great-grandparents are buried there."

"My grandfather? I already have two grandfathers. How can that be?" I asked. My other grandfather, tall and austere and remote, not at all like the adventurous youth I had imagined gathering languages around Europe, lived in a tall austere house in England. I had only met him twice.

"Because my father is only your step-grandfather really, your mother and I are only half-sisters."

I had not realised that there were people buried there, nobody had told me that before, and nobody had ever mentioned my real grandfather either, as far as I could remember. They must have thought I was too small, too uncomprehending. Grown-ups are like that, even the ones who tell one quite a lot about some things, still keep all sorts of other things, interesting things, from small children.

"Tell me about him," I asked Kay.

"I don't really know much about him," she said.

"Then I'll go and ask Gran."

"Don't you dare!" she said sharply. "Don't you dare!" she repeated.

I was dumbstruck by her vehemence, and my lip must have quivered, because she suddenly put her arms around me.

"Look" she said, "I am only thinking of Gran. When I was a little girl she sometimes used to go there and weep. Then for days afterwards she would look miserable. That is why my father planted several more circles of trees around the circle of trees already there, so close together that even when the trees were small they completely hid the graves from the house. Then he put in a borehole and windmill, just to water them, and a fence. I'll tell you all I know, but then please don't mention to Gran that you went there.

"From what I can gather, this real grandfather of yours was very handsome and charming, a talented musician. In fact, I've heard it said that the whole family was artistic in one way or another. The only drawback was that he was Dutch, and Gran came from an English family who disapproved of what in those days they called a mixed marriage, so Gran had to defy her family to marry your grandfather. She was madly in love and went ahead with the marriage despite their objections.

Two years after the wedding her husband was dead, and so was his only brother, I think, but I am not sure, that it was in the great influenza plague which wiped out millions of people, especially the young and healthy.

Gran was left with this huge property, which must have been terribly isolated in the days of horses and wagons, and two baby daughters, estranged from her family. My father, who had known her before this other marriage, married her and took over the first husband's farm."

"And the other grave?" I asked.

"That is where both your great-grandparents lie. They died only a year or two apart, a few years before their sons. All gone, the whole family, in a span of seven years.

"There now, I have told you more or less everything I know, because I don't want you to go worrying Gran. She is happy now, and I believe that you'll only bring up old forgotten grief if you probe."

So I never said a word about it to Gran. I could not imagine my cheerful Gran weeping, but I dreaded taking the risk of saying anything that could possibly make her sad. I have never mentioned it to my mother either; the subject seems taboo. Words float in the air, allusions, intimations of aspersions cast by the wife of my father's eldest brother, lingering prejudices that deeply wounded my mother.

The graves changed me a little inside even then, and though I still loved him, and he still spoiled me, from that moment, inside my head, I always thought of the man I had believed was my grandfather, as my step-grandfather.

For a long time I did not go back to that strange and secretive place, but then once more I was inexorably drawn by that magic circle, by the melancholy yearning I felt in that place, and by the beauty of the sculptures.

Once, months later, my curiosity was fed by a book on Greek Art that an uncle from England let me look at. As I browsed through it, through the flat, grey images in the book, there seemed to echo and resonate in my mind the solid presence of the marble forms in the graveyard. Then I realised. The Winged Victory of Samothrace reminded me of the young girl with the beautiful face, high on her plinth. But how? In what way? The Victory had wings, and no head, no face; the real statue had a head, but no wings. But the billowing drapery had the same feeling of turbulence, and something else, something about the whole figure, I could not quite define; a sense of surging energy, of striding confidently, almost joyously into the wind, into an opposing force.

Then the shapes of the Greek vases in the book. Exactly the same shape as the huge black granite Grecian urns high, high on the other two plinths. But not the same. The ones in the book were pottery.

Names too, echoed and resonated, but were not quite the same. "Head of Alexander the Great" and the word "hellenic" used over and over again under many plates in the book. What did it mean?

One of the brothers (was it my real grandfather?) had as Christian names, the strange names, Helenus Alexander.

Odd, I thought, the way some things, some images, some names, sounds, smells, recur in one's life, and form little repeat patterns, like echoes of echoes.

Those grey pictures of ancient Apollos also gave me the clearest picture of my secret grandfather. A vivid image for that secret picture gallery in my mind: young, forever very young; broad, noble forehead, straight nose, firmly chiselled chin, and fine wide-set eyes, gazing intently, but blankly, the way marble eyes in marble sculptures gaze blankly, at the future he never had.

At that time, though, I was young, too small to ponder on such things for long. It was all too confusing, too much to understand, so I turned my mind to simpler things, things I loved, things like climbing mountains.

CHAPTER SEVEN

THE SPIRIT OF THE LITTLE PEOPLE

"See the mountains kiss high heaven."

PERCY BYSSHE SHELLEY

Memories of the mountains pervade my consciousness of those days. Mountains reaching up to the sky; the Earth straining upwards, yearning to be one with her consort, the Heavens.

And truly, there were times when my mountains seemed to be as much part of the heavens as of the earth.

Summer storms were ferociously, tumultuously orchestrated in those mountains; wild, billowing clouds, black as night, would come surging in, shrouding the peaks, then breaking as torrential, furious waves washing over the cliffs. Whips of lightning would crack into the basalt spires, echoed by resounding crashing as boulders and overhangs broke away, to be hurled, smashing into the ravines between.

Then suddenly there would be calm; the rain and mist and steam would settle into the valleys, obliterating the lower slopes, while the uppermost krantzes and spires and pinnacles would float above the blanket of clouds; tons-heavy granite and basalt formations would hover there, weightless, floating in the pristine, storm-washed sky.

Mountains have many moods. Moods that seem to emanate from within the secret depths of the mountains themselves, not imposed upon them by the weather or storms. Sometimes on bleak winter's days, when the wind whistled and keened through the narrow gorges, those cloven, fissured Mountains of the Dragon became scary, sinister; jagged and bleak and bare. Rent asunder by some dark primaeval upheaval.

At other times they were benign, pretty as a picture, painted in beautiful blues, and hues of mauves and violets against deep ultra-marine shadows. Then climbing them seemed irresistible.

I climbed as soon as I could walk, for the simple reason that the mountains were there, and one could not explore far without climbing. And if as a toddler I was reportedly always saying "up, up, up" there need be no deeper meaning to that than the fact that it is easier for a small child to climb up. Boulders and ledges which seem only challengingly difficult on the way up, can be terrifyingly daunting coming down again.

My first challenge would have been the "koppie" behind the house. I cannot remember when I first conquered it, but it must have been an exhilarating experience, because I continued to love it, and climb it often, and it was the first place I went to when I returned from England. A *koppie* (from the Dutch *kopje* meaning "little head") is a conical hill, which, while not necessarily very high or very impressive, gives one a 360 degree view from the summit. Funny that people should see mountains as heads; I recently read that in Australia the mountains that are called the Olgas are called Kata Tjuta by the Aborigines, which means "many heads".

From the koppie I progressed to the main range, with my little band of brown companions, though at first we stuck to the gentler rocky slopes, near the house, well below the steep vertical cliffs along the top of the ridge that formed the spiky spine of the Dragon Mountains.

Then gradually, as the months went by, we became more adventurous, and tried to climb higher and higher, but there seemed no way of scaling that rocky spine, with its sheer sides of shiny granite. In some places we could clamber and climb a little way up, but sooner or later we would be up against an unassailable rock face.

Until one day we explored a fissure; a narrow, ravine-like break in the cliff face. It was as if, eons ago, when the mountain could still move like a dragon, it had heaved and twisted too violently and split its spine.

"Look!" exclaimed one of the children. "The way it has cracked has made steps up the side." Not little household steps, but great waist-high zig-zag gouges, continuous enough for us to be able to heave and pull each other up. We emerged at the top panting and excited, high on the heady champagne of reaching such unassailable heights, oohing and aahing at our own daring.

"We must be at the very top of the world!" said Iris in an awestruck voice.

"The very top of the world!" echoed the others.

"From here you can see forever!" I said, and I was almost right; we could see mountains and ridges, the wrinkled, writhing surface of the earth, falling away towards the distant invisible ocean which I knew lay far, far to the east. From the house one felt surrounded, almost hemmed in by mountains and hills, but from this height the world expanded and stretched out to an infinitely distant horizon.

From this height our own familiar world took on a strange new perspective. The homestead and shearing shed and out-buildings looked like tiny stone doll's houses, and the dark green trees like toy-box trees, laid on a mat of uncharacteristic green in the arid landscape The tractor, parked outside the shearing shed, looked like a miniature matchbox toy, and two people walking between the house and shed looked no bigger than ants. The graveyard grove looked like a dark green ring on the reddish earth.

Apart from our farm, and the circle of huts, there was virtually no evidence of man's intrusion on the landscape, not a single neighbouring homestead could be seen, even from this height. Only the narrow dirt road, twisting and turning, this way and that, like a snake trying to find the rare, narrow passes through the rows of mountains to the south-east, and even that was almost completely camouflaged, like a rocky, fossilised snake.

The excited commentary continued for a long time. At last we turned away from the vast panorama to the east.

"Let's see what the other side of the world looks like!" So we clambered and crawled the short distance to the western edge of the precipice.

There we learned, like so many before us, that the summit we had reached was not the ultimate goal, or even the top of the world.

Because the range at this point had slit into two ridges, so that behind the main range of mountains was a narrow chasm; steep and rocky, and beyond that another range, higher, not much higher, but higher, than the one we had climbed, and behind that again rose the summit that was the highest peak in this region. We did not let this dis-covery distract from the excitement of reaching the top, but nor were we tempted to explore this new alien landscape, cut off and hidden from our familiar world. For months we were content to explore along of the top of the home range, where we could still keep in touch with the familiar, still see the homestead and the huts.

That winter was bitterly cold. For weeks a dusting of snow shrouded the peaks, making them look pale and ghostly in the evening light. The dams and water troughs froze over, and even on clear days, the biting frosts and chilling winds kept us indoors, or in sheltered nooks in the sun, making clay oxen, or playing games with knuckle-bones, or examining our broken china collection with all the intensity of a stamp-collector checking stamps.

Our broken china collection all started accidentally, with an accident. Ethel and Iris and Dinah and Gran and I were in the kitchen when Dinah broke one of Gran's best bone china tea-cups. The grown-ups were both so upset that Ethel, the little peacemaker, quickly swept up the pieces in her bare hands, and said she would put them on the rubbish tip. Iris and I followed her out of the back door, a little way up the hill behind the house, to a hollow between some rocks. She was about to throw the remains of the teacup over the rock when Iris picked a piece out of her hands.

"Look, pretty, one red rose all by itself."

Then I picked out a piece I liked, this time a yellow rose with a green leaf.

Ethel threw the rest away, but then retrieved from the tip a shard of bone china with a blue cornflower on it. We were aimlessly wandering back to the house, each admiring our own tiny piece of flower-decorated porcelain, when suddenly we all, without saying a word to one another, veered off in the direction of the gardening shed, ran in and each grabbed a small spade or fork or hoe. We often did this, the three of us; we simultaneously had a new idea, exactly the same idea, about what to do next. Wielding our digging tool we raced back to the dump and started digging. Now, these days I would find the thought of looking into a rubbish tip disgusting, but there was nothing revolting about the dump on the farm; it had very little else in it, apart from broken china.

Things we throw in the bin in the city, like food packaging and food scraps did not exist there. Almost all the food was homegrown so did not come in packages, and all the bought food came in bags, bags of flour and beans and sugar, even small cotton bags for things like salt. These bags were never thrown out, but used over and over again as bags, or cut up for dish-cloths. Leftover food in the serving dishes was always taken back to the huts by Dinah or the inside girls, leftovers on plates were added to the kitchen scraps and fed to the free-range chickens and turkeys who gobbled up every scrap. Bones were fed to the dogs. The ashes from the fireplace and the stove were thrown, still glowing, each morning, down the infinite depths of the pit-toilet. Any discarded newspapers or magazines were keenly sought after by the maids to take home to start their cooking fires.

There were no electric appliances to go wrong, the old flat-irons were made of solid iron and would last a hundred years, and instead of a fridge there was a wire cage with walls a foot thick filled with cinders, and with water always seeping through, which had been there for years. Yet very little food ever went into that coolchest, most of it went straight from production to consumption. The milkmaid milked the few cows before breakfast, so that we had fresh frothy milk for our porridge, then only a little jugful was saved for afternoon tea, the rest was fed to the cats or orphan lambs or dogs or given to the maids to make their calabash yoghurt. A cow was milked again for supper. Once a week the milk was "separated" to make cream and butter.

Eggs were collected, often by me and Iris and Ethel, before breakfast, for breakfast, from the hens' hiding places around the outhouses and gardens. When there were too many, Gran told us to leave certain wisely chosen nest sites, to let the pile of eggs in them accumulate until the hens became broody and sat on them. In winter when the hens went off the lay we simply did not have eggs. I loved collecting eggs, holding their lovely shapes in my hands, sometimes newly laid and still warm; then gazing at them all together in the basket, arranged like beautiful, small sculptures. The luscious vegetables and salads that grew in the garden in summer were only picked to go straight into the next meal. Some were always left to go to seed, to be gathered for the next season.

All this meant that there was no revolting rubbish; the dump that we were digging in had very little else in it. Only these shards of broken pottery and china were quite useless to everyone else, and thrown here because they could not be used for some other purpose.

After a while Gran came out to see what we were doing. We had spread our favourite pieces on a nearby rock. Flower patterns, violets, poppies, an English garden with hollyhocks, even delicately painted ladies and gentlemen wearing white wigs in idyllic landscapes.

"I remember that cup," she said, "and that was a limoge vase I kept on my dressing table." Then she looked with interest at all the rest. "I do not recognise any of these, these must all be from before my time."

I was astonished. Gran went back to "the olden days." These shards then must go back to older times, to the first white women in these wild, wild mountains; women wrenched from gentle, closetted lives, with only tiny tokens of gentility like these fine bone china fragments to remind them of their past. As we dug deeper, many, many fragments seemed to come from the same dinner set. It was made of the finest porcelain, so thin and delicate that when we held the pieces up to the light we could see our fingers through the translucent whiteness. The porcelain itself was sculpted into patterns, swirls and flutes and scrolls and seashells, and over the sculptural patterns, handpainted flowers trimmed with pure gold. I found myself wondering whether it belonged to the lady in the graveyard; whether all those pieces from one dinner set had broken, gradually, one by one, over the years, in tiny accidents like the one in the kitchen that day. Or perhaps she was the first one, perhaps she had arrived, not to a ready-built house, but to live in a tent, while the men went about the laborious task of cutting mountain stone, getting a stonemason to build the house. Perhaps when at last the house was built she had unpacked the trunk only to find most of her lovely china already smashed on the journey.

For a while we loved our china collection, loved to pick over the pieces and wonder at the shapes and patterns and colours. Yet even diversions like these could only interest us for a little while, and only in the icy depths of winter, when it was too cold to climb the mountains.

Then one day, we decided, suddenly after breakfast, that the time had come to start mountain climbing again, time to summon our little band of companions. The days were lengthening slightly, the sun was shining, and in the lea of the hill behind the house, the wind seemed to have abated; but once we were high on the mountainside the wind regained its momentum, buffetting us, making us lose our balance, slicing through our loosely knit woollen jerseys with a biting chilling edge.

Our jerseys were all handknitted by the old aunts. During the war the two old ladies had spent most of their days knitting socks of coarse khaki wool to send to the troops. They seemed to argue endlessly about the best pattern for "turning a heel." Afterwards, when the war was over, and they turned to knitting jerseys, the competition seemed to be who could finish a garment first: and so as the years went by they knitted with bigger and bigger needles. This meant that when the wind was strong and icy it cut right through the open knit. I was wearing a jersey specially made for me that winter, striped, made of all the left-over colours, but rather short, so that it left a little gap at my waist where it did not quite meet my dungarees. (I suppose the quicker to finish it!) The others were all wearing hand-me-downs, from Kay or Gran or John or the Aunts themselves. Only Ethel and Iris had anything under their jerseys, the denim pinafores that Gran made for them. There were a couple of advantages, however, to the hand-me-downs. They had shrunk, matting the wool, making them denser and less open, and also they were big; far too big for their wearers, more like knee-length tunics than jerseys.

Of course in spring and summer and autumn the other children were the lucky ones, they could go stark naked all day. When I protested that that privilege should be extended to me, the grown-ups said that my skin was a problem, that I would burn sore and red as a tomato in that high mountain sun. Some painful experiences eventually convinced me that they were right.

The higher we climbed the more the icy wind penetrated our open knits, so we did not dawdle and explore, or search for tortoises, or examine flowers in our usual fashion. We needed to keep moving, keep climbing to keep from freezing. When we reached the ravine with the steps to our home summit, Ethel said cautiously,

"If we go to the top today the wind will surely pick us up and blow us away."

So we went, for the first time, through the fissure, into the alien valley beyond, where there was some slight shelter from the relentless wind.

As we moved into unfamiliar territory we unwittingly changed formation. Coming up the familiar slopes we had swarmed up, now one ahead, then another, now six abreast, now in two's or three's. But here, in this eerie, rocky moonscape land, where there were no living creatures to be seen, not even dassies, no trees, hardly any vegetation at all in winter apart from the grey-green lichens on the rocks, I found myself striding ahead, like the archetypal explorer with bearers, single file behind. I set a cracking pace, partly to keep warm, but mostly to stifle the uneasiness I felt, in this strange and unfamiliar part of the mountains. We found that we could avoid going down into the ravine and could skirt around on a ridge that linked the two ranges, so soon we were climbing the steep slopes of the higher range. It was, surprisingly, not cautious Ethel, but the two little boys who protested.

"We have gone far enough. We must not go higher."

"Why?" I said.

"Because the high places are inhabited by the spirits of the little people," they replied.

"Who are the little people?"

But the boys lowered their eyes. "We do not know."

I had encountered this kind of secrecy before. Boys, older than these two, were being tutored in the folk-lore of the tribe before being initiated as men, and they sometimes confided in their younger brothers; it was forbidden to pass on certain knowledge to women and girls. I knew it was no good questioning them further, but in a way it also goaded me into wanting to reach the crest, so I continued to climb, with my entourage lagging behind. Suddenly, as we topped a crest, I pointed.

"There," I cried. "There is one of your spirits. Look, he is lying, reclining but at the same time guarding the pass. There is his head, and he is leaning on one arm. His knees are up and his legs are so big there is a cave underneath."

"No," sighed the little boy patiently. "That is a rock. Spirits are not rocks. Spirits are shadows."

So I hurried on to see if the rock formation resembled a reclining figure as vividly from close up.

"Look," I exclaimed, "It even looks like a head from close up, and an arm, and huge legs, but from here the cave under the knees looks like a tunnel!"

As we stood and looked at the rock formation, the rock-figure seemed to take on a brooding, supernatural, mythic presence, to be half-alive, and the mood of the mountains shifted, although there was no change at all in the weather. The sky remained cloudless, but turned a pale acidic green-blue, and the weak, watery winter sun withdrew what warmth there was. The intense silence took on an enigmatic strangeness, seemed sinister in the cold, clear light.

We stood there, stiff and silent as statues, as the wind froze the thin film of perspiration on our cheeks so that I imagined that we were wearing masks of ice.

I shivered with apprehension, and was about to say, "Well, let's head for home now," when one of the little boys took the words from right out of my mouth.

"We MUST head for home now," he said urgently.

If I had managed to get my words in first, or if Ethel, who had some authority over me had said them, we would have left straight away, but some strange perverseness in me, some rebellion at the emphasis on "must" from a little boy smaller than I was, made me say,

"We have come all this way! Let's at least see what is on the other side of the tunnel."

I think I half hoped that they would protest again, but nobody said anything, and for a while we stood there, indecisively, shivering with cold and apprehension.

Then I turned, and crawled through the narrow tunnel, wondering if I would be going all alone, but the others followed, reluctantly close behind.

As I stood up on the other side, I gasped.

"The spirit of the little people!"

Behind me I heard, echoing my whisper, my friends gasping in unison. "The shadow spirit of the little people!"

A stone clattered down into the gorge below, and I felt and heard, rather than saw, my companions reversing with all haste, back through the tunnel. But I could not move. I was frozen with fear, petrified into immobility, because there before me, in front of the high peak, stood the towering Shadow Spirit. Its head was three quarters of the way up the monolith, one arm was outstretched to hold a spear, while in the other it held a huge shield that covered his body.

Then my ears picked up a strange mesmerising song, that reminded me of both the plaintive keening and ululating of the native women at a funeral, and yet at the same time it made me think of the haunting notes of the pan-flute I had heard one of my mother's musician friends play in London.

In the stillness and silence of the mountains, those high-pitched notes seemed to resonate with a menacing, threatening, insistent hum; echoing and re-echoing through my mind, making me tremble with terror.

I felt the hairs on the back of my neck bristle. The sound grew louder as though the spirit were advancing towards me, but still I could not make my frozen limbs move.

Then it seemed it was not only imperceptibly advancing, but also changing shape, the shield became triangular rather than oval; and the arms seemed to be moving up in a gesture, that at first seemed threatening, and then to change, in the strangest way, almost to a greeting. The head did not move, it continued to stare down at me.

I was swaying now, mesmerised, ready to throw myself down into the black shadowy ravine, if the spirit advanced any closer. I squeezed my eyes closed, my mind reeling, all reason deserting me.

Then, inexplicably, I thought of Father.

"There is a logical explanation for nearly everything," he had once said. "But you must open your eyes and really look."

I still could not move my head but I wrenched my eyes open and looked around.

The sun was low in the north-west, casting a sharp shadow on the side of the high peak. And now, when I really looked with my eyes open, I saw that the shadow had changed shape again, and no longer resembled a figure. It transformed before my eyes into the shadow in relief of the cliff formation, only the head remained, and I saw now that there was the opening of a cave, high on the high peak. The singing, keening, continued, but it seemed lower pitched, more melodious, less threatening, almost a song of welcome. I tried to convince myself that it was made by the wind whistling through the conical tunnel under the rocks; or perhaps there really were women singing at a funeral far far away, many mountains away, and what I was hearing was the echo of echoes of echoes.

The strangest thing was, that now that I could no longer see a figure in the shadows, now that I had given myself a logical explanation for the haunting keening, I felt more convinced than ever that there was a presence there, a spirit of the mountains, a spirit that had been hostile at first, but now seemed simply to infuse me with a sense of wonder and strange longings.

At last, I found that I could move. I spun around and crawled frantically back through the tunnel, grazing my knees, and bumping my head, in my haste.

On the other side sat my friends. They too, were petrified with fear. Petrified into a little circular cairn of knee-hugging rocks. Too frightened to crawl back through the narrow tunnel to rescue me, yet equally terrified at the thought of facing their elders if they returned without their charge.

"It's all right." I told them. "It was only a shadow."

"But we told you, spirits are shadows," said the boys.

"It changed shape," I said.

"Spirits can change shape," persisted the boys patiently. "It is the way of spirits to change shape."

"No, it was the sun moving. The sun was low in the sky."

Suddenly, Ethel jumped up. "The sun is low in the sky!" she exclaimed.

It was as if she had been electrified into action. We all jumped up and started running, leaping, scrambling back the way we had come.

Once we reached the cleft in the home range, and were back on familiar territory, where we knew every rock and ridge, we picked up speed, leaping down the mountainside with the grace and agility of a herd of Grant's gazelles pursued by a lion. But we were not being chased by a lion, we were spurred on by fear. The brown children only by fear of the spirit, I also in fear of the wrath of my grandmother if we arrived home after dark.

Now, to an outsider my grandmother might seem to allow me unbridled freedom, and very little discipline, but I knew that, though she made very few rules, and most of those rules were about how one treated other people, as far as those few rules were concerned, she expected explicit and complete obedience. One rule was that if we went mountain climbing we should always be home before sunset. I could imagine her saying briefly, but with utter finality.

"You were not back before sunset. Now you are no longer allowed up the mountain."

We were onto the gentler slopes now, among the thorn bushes

and dried grass, following a path made by sheep and humans. The sun had slipped behind the granite-black mountains and the ground was dark and shadowy against the luminescent acidic green of the brief late-winter dusk. Our stride lengthened, and when the path branched, three children took the path to the circle of huts, and three continued towards the welcoming yellow-gold beacon of the newly lit lantern glowing through the uncurtained window of the kitchen.

There was a figure standing silhouetted against the lamplight, in the kitchen door, and I was sure it must be Gran, waiting to deliver her edict.

It was only when we came right up to her that we realised that it was Dinah. She started berating us, particularly cautious and sensible Ethel, because she was the oldest, and because she was supposed to be my minder, my protector.

I interrupted her.

"Where is my grandmother?"

"She has been in the office all afternoon, working on the books. I did not want to disturb her." Poor Dinah must have been in a quandary for the last half-hour, wondering whether to report our lateness. No wonder she was so angry.

I sighed with relief. Once every few months, Gran shut herself in her little office and "did the books". It was obviously not a task she relished but she tackled it with concentration and determination, not emerging until she had solved whatever problem they presented.

She would not have noticed that we were late.

I tried to distract Dinah who was still giving us a tongue lashing.

"Dinah, we are starving. We took no food with us. Did you keep dinner for us?"

She went to the oven and brought out three plates of pot-roasted mutton, potatoes and pumpkin. Dinah cooked in a big cast iron pot on the iron stove, and she could make a the most delicious pot-roast that I have ever tasted. The meat all crispy brown on the outside, and tender tasty inside. Potatoes brown, just short of burnt brown and salty on the outside, fluffy and white inside; and best of all her pumpkin, glazed transparent amber gold, caramelly sweet. The only green on the plate was a dark, dull green little patch of mint sauce. By early spring all the greens in the vegetable garden were gone, and even the rows of bottled beans in the pantry were used up, so we were faced with a few weeks without greens at all until the spring peas were ready.

"Dinah, you are the very best cook in the whole world."

As I had hoped, the tongue-lashing modified into gentler scolding. Dinner was a midday meal at the homestead. My young aunts and uncle protested that it was much more sophisticated to have dinner in the evening like their city friends, and even my grandfather often said it would be more convenient in the evening, but Gran was adamant.

"Midday is a more convenient time for Dinah. She comes in to cook breakfast and then dinner, so that she is free to go home in the afternoons and cook for her husband."

Gran and the aunts prepared a simple cold supper and the "inside girls" took it in turns to wash up.

Today Dinah had spent the afternoon in the warm kitchen doing her beadwork and, as the afternoon wore on, had waited for the return of the girls. Now she was scolding her daughters again.

"Quickly, we must hurry home to feed your father. It is lucky that I cooked his samp and beans here today."

So as soon as the girls had eaten, Dinah tied the bowl of hot food into an old tablecloth, knotting the opposite corners, gave it to the girls to carry, and bustled them out into the cold night air. I went to find Gran.

She was just putting the books away. She had not realised that we had been late.

"Gran" I said. "Who are the little people?"

"Which little people?"

"The little people who lived in the mountains."

"You must mean the Bushmen."

"Did they live in these mountains?"

"Yes," said Gran. "The Bushmen, together perhaps with the Hottentots, were the original people, the aboriginal people of the whole of Southern Africa.

"They were stoneage hunters and gatherers, small, agile, apricot-yellow people, who lived in complete harmony with nature for thousands and thousands of years. Then a few hundred years ago, the bigger, darker Bantu people, tribes like the Xhosas and the Zulus, who were herders of cattle, started moving south, first along the fertile coastal hills and eventually up into these parts. It is possible that the Bushmen started hunting the Bantu cattle, especially in times of drought. Whatever the reason, the Bantu mercilessly hunted the Bushmen. At first, they appear to have retreated to the rugged terrain of these mountains, too high and steep and arid for the Bantu cattle, and too difficult to wage assagai warfare. But the march of history was against them. They were small gentle people who made no claim on the land, and killed only for food, while the Xhosas and the Zulus were big, strong, warlike and territorial, so many of the Bushmen were driven across the central desert, and then of course the Europeans arrived and added to the push for grazing land, so that now there are only a few pure Bushmen left in these mountains, most of the survivors of their race live in the Kalahari Desert, far to the west of here."

"How do you know this?" I asked.

"Their paintings!" said Gran. "The Bushmen make quite extraordinarily beautiful cave paintings, but none of the Bantu tribes do. Many,

many cave paintings have been found in these mountains."

"On our farm?"

"Not that I know of," said Gran, "but there could be. The ones that have survived are usually in high and remote caves. Come, let us see what the encyclopaedia has to say."

There, under Bushmen of the Kalahari, we found an entry describing the life of these small stoneage hunters. There was also a photograph of one of their paintings. Little stick figure hunters, crudely drawn, pursuing a herd of antelope, and these, I could see, even in the small black and white photograph, were beautifully, sensitively portrayed; full of vitality and movement.

I pored over the picture long after Gran had left to prepare supper.

Then with a sigh I returned the volume to the bookcase. For a moment I stared at the whole row of twenty thick books, the whole encyclopaedia, so good for finding facts and pictures, so useless when one had real questions. The questions that gnawed at my mind were:

"What is real?"

"Did I see and hear a real Spirit?"

My friends all believed implicitly and unwaveringly in the reality of the spirit. My imagination and my instinct and my intuition wanted to agree with my friends, but on the other hand, my reason and my logic said that there could be natural explanations for the things that I had seen and heard that day. So what is real? What is true?

Somewhere deep down, I felt that the only hope of finding out was to climb again to the far range, and this time to reach the secret, hidden cave on the high peak.

CHAPTER EIGHT

SWEETS, SUGAR, COFFEE AND TOBACCO

"Look and you will find.

What is unsought will go undetected."

SOPHOCLES

Recalling the terror in the eyes of my friends, I knew that they would not go lightly to the far range again, let alone up the high peak. I would have to make a plan.

At supper that evening I asked my young aunt, "Kay, it is shopping day soon, isn't it?"

"Yes, John and I are going to do the shopping tomorrow. You can come along if you'd like to."

So the next day we set out in the old lorry for the long and bumpy ride to the small outpost. Usually, if I went, Ethel and Iris came too, and all three of us sat in the back of the lorry; but the day was icy cold and it was even windier than the day before, so I had to squeeze in between my aunt and uncle in the front cabin.

At the general store, which was one of the few buildings on the wide main street of the tiny town, John drove the truck around to the back entrance and began loading large bags of mealie-meal, dried beans and flour and dark brown sugar and coffee and rolls of chewing tobacco onto the back of the lorry, a month's supply, not only for the farmhouse but rations for all the natives of the kraal. I loved their combined smell. The sickly sweet molassy smell of the brown "government sugar", the pungent odour of the chewing tobacco and the aromatic ground Kenya coffee, seemed to mingle into a single aroma that I still remember so well. I would always go to help my grandfather dole out the rations from the little storeroom in the stable complex, cool and dark because it was built of huge stone blocks, just to savour that aroma.

Now, however, I had other business. I went inside the shop, dark and secretive after the glaring light outside. At one end a man presided over tools and hardware, at the other an old woman sat knitting, beside her counter next to a pot-bellied stove. On the counter were rows of glass jars containing an assortment of sweets. Behind the counter were shelves with bolts of cloth and spools of lace and ribbon.

"I'd like to buy some sweets," I said to the old lady, who laid down her knitting and pushed herself awkwardly out of her chair and went around behind the counter.

"How many?"

"As many as I can buy with this much money," I replied, turning my money box upside down and spilling the contents onto the counter. There were florins and shillings and sixpences and tickeys and pennies and ha'pennies and farthings and even half a crown, from my last birthday.

"I want some of those, and those and those," I said, "and also some... chocolates!"

"That's a lot of money to be spending on sweets. What will your grandmother say?"

"She won't mind."

So the old lady counted and divided the money into four piles to make it easier for herself.

"This money will buy you two pounds of barley sugars," she said, weighing them in her balancing scales, putting brass weights in the other scale.

"And this is for the licorice." Again she weighed carefully.

"Now some nigger balls," I said.

The name of those sweets still rolls off my tongue as easily as those round balls of sweetness rolled around our tongues, because for most of my life I had not the slightest idea that both words could have other connotations.

I realise now, how perilously close I had come to using their name to Miss Ashburn. She had been asking us each to describe our favourite food and I had very nearly, in my innocence, said "I adore sucking nigger balls." Instead I had said, "I like chewing biltong!"

"What's that?" she had asked, and I had told her it was dried, raw meat, and she had grimaced and glared at me coldly as if I were making it up to annoy her.

Perversely now, I wish I really had said to her "I adore sucking nigger balls!" Furious apoplexy, especially in hindsight, is much more fun than cold glaring!

"Nigger" was not a word used at that time, on that farm, and I had never ever heard it used except for these sweets. Which is not to say that there was not a local equivalent, which at that time, and in that place was "kaffir". Rude white men in towns used it. "Bloody kaffirs." I once heard one swear, "Bloody lazy kaffirs."

I was absolutely forbidden to ever call anyone a "kaffir". I was convinced that it was a swearword, but when I looked it up in a dictionary, wondering whether they put swearwords in a dictionary, I realised that it did not start out that way, it is an Arabic word that means "unbeliever". The white men and Arabs must have thought that if the natives did not believe in their version of God, then believing in their own Gods and their own Spirits was not believing at all; people always seem to judge people from their own belief systems.

By the time I heard the word "kaffir", it had come to be considered rude.

I was only allowed to use the word "native". But words, even words that one uses everyday can be confusing when one is very young. "Native" to me meant my brown friends, but in Gran's library I noticed a book called *The Return of the Native*, by Thomas Hardy. None of Gran's other books seemed to deal with natives, so I took it out of the bookcase.

"That is not a book you will enjoy just yet," said Gran. "Besides, the native of the title is an Englishman." It took me a long time to work that one out!

The old lady in the shop put each scale-scoop of sweets into a brown paper bag. Last of all the chocolates, which came from under the counter. They were sold by number, not by weight, and the old lady counted them out aloud as she put them into another brown bag. I put the paper bags into the leather skin bag I had brought along and skipped back to the lorry where I carefully placed it in a gap between the rolls of tobacco. Then I pulled it out again, took out two chocolates and shoved it back into its niche. I jumped down and offered a chocolate each to Kay and John.

Back home I emptied all the sweets onto a large tray and then carefully divided them into seven equal piles. These I slipped into the seven large cardboard cones, like over-sized ice-cream cones, that I had rolled and glued early that morning. Then I folded down the tops to make a tight lid. Pleased with my efforts, I grabbed one and ran off, up the path that led to the circle of huts.

My friends must have seen me coming, because by the time I was halfway there, they had run down the path to meet me. They must also have noticed the large cardboard cone in my hands, but no one asked about it. Instead Iris said, "Did you have a nice day in town?"

"Yes" I replied. "But tomorrow I want to climb the mountain again. Tomorrow I want to reach the cave on the high peak."

Ethel objected first this time.

"It is too far. Yesterday, we only reached home after the sun was down."

"Yesterday we only left in the middle of the morning. Tomorrow we will leave as soon as the sun rises. We will take breakfast as well as lunch."

So the boys put in their objections.

"The spirit of the little people will be angry if we come once more." Their eyes were wide with apprehension.

"Oh," I said casually. "We will take him an offering. See this?" and I held up the cardboard cone.

I knew that they had all seen, and wondered, but had been too polite to ask, although it bore a remarkable resemblance to the paper cones full of sweets they were always given at Christmas. I unfolded the top.

"See, it is full of sweets; all sorts, even chocolates. I made one for the spirit and one exactly the same for each of you for lunch. That is, if you would like to come."

For a moment they stood, silent, their eyes fixed on the chocolates.

Then they all said in unison, "We would like to come!"

"Good!" I said. "Then we must go back and ask Dinah if we can have a picnic breakfast as well as lunch tomorrow."

It is funny how, kneeling here with my rock in my hand, being transported back to those times, reliving those days so vividly, almost feeling that I am back there, every now and again for just a moment I slip back into a more knowing fourteen-year-old perspective. Now remembering how I used the sweets to persuade my friends, I wonder if that could have been a form of bribery. Yet in those days it was very simple to me. I loved the mountains and especially wanted to reach the cave, my friends loved sweets and especially chocolates; this way it seemed to me then, we were all getting what we especially wanted.

Gran's few rules seemed simple to me then too, but I realise now how seriously she enforced them, above all, her rule about treating others with consideration. Gran had high standards of consideration. I was going to say morality, but that sounds religious, yet she did not seem to be religious in the conventional sense of going to church, though more than once I heard her say "Do unto others…"

I also heard her quote Nietzsche, "When the exceptional human being treats the mediocre more tenderly than himself and his peers, this is not mere politeness of heart, it is his DUTY." She said this because she was angry, very angry with someone who had been rude to a native.

"If you think you are more civilised, then the only way to prove it, is by being more civilised," she had finished coldly.

She said something similar one day to a friend as they sat watching the young adults playing tennis, from the shade of her garden.

"This notion of superiority carries with it a great responsibility. It could not be justified unless one could oneself maintain the very highest standards of nobility and compassion and civility, at all times."

It was said, I thought to myself, eavesdropping, in a chiding tone of voice, especially the emphasis on "at all times".

My own most vivid brush with this attitude concerned white children. There were no children anywhere near my age, on any of the neighbouring farms but, in that nearest little town, where we had gone to buy supplies, really little more than a ghost-town railway outpost, there was an orphanage, or children's refuge, run by some Presbyterian missionaries. In that same little outpost were several "poor white" families living in the railway cottages along the line. The men must once have worked for the railways, been needed to hook up the double engines that were used to pull the carriages up through the mountain passes, but now that roads were improving slightly, and more people had cars, there was a lot of talk about cutbacks in the railways, so there was less work for the men.

One of the farmers, who had no children, and who considered himself a philanthropist, used to have a Christmas party for the orphans and all the children of the town and the district.

Now nearly three months before Christmas, Kay had come home from Durban, where she now lived with a friend some of the time, bringing a dress for my birthday. Kay loved pretty things, flowery, feminine, pretty things. One had only to walk into her bedroom on the farm to see this. The curtains were a pretty print, pink and apricot and white roses on grey-green leaves, and they had frills all around the edges and were tied back with elaborate bows. Between the frills were lace curtains. Her bed repeated the roses and frills and lace, even her pillows had frills all around them. Now the dress she bought for me outdid even her bedroom! I was absolutely bowled over by that dress, it was like no dress I had ever seen before. All pink lace and net, all frills and flounces and furbelows, all ribbons and bows! The very antithesis of the grey flannel dungarees I wore in winter and the simple cotton shifts I wore in summer. But apart from prancing around in it on my birthday, I had had no opportunity to wear it. So as soon as I heard about the party I started daydreaming.

I dreamed of wafting into the old church hall like Cinderella at the ball, and as in the story of Cinderella, everyone gasping and murmuring, "Who can that be, in that lovely lacy dress?" And Father Christmas saying, as he handed me my present, "Why you look like a fairytale princess in that frilly, fairy dress!"

It was not until the very day of the party, the very hour of our departure, that Gran realised my intention of wearing the dress.

"Just think for a moment how the orphans and all the poor children will feel when they see you in that dress. The girls will wish they had a dress like that too, and feel dissatisfied with their own simple clothes. This is their treat, you wouldn't want to spoil it for them would you?"

I can still, with absolute clarity, remember the dress I ended up wearing to that Christmas party. Pale washed-out, almost colourless green; linen, no lace; very simple, no waistline, no belt, no full skirt, no frills, no bows, just the tiniest little white embroidered flower on the collar.

CHAPTER NINE

THE BUSHMAN STONE

"When we reach the mountain summits, we leave behind us all the things that weigh heavily down below on our body and our spirit. We feel a new freedom, a gentle exhilaration, an exaltation of the body no less than spirit. We feel a great joy."

JAN SMUTS

The day after my trip to town to buy sweets, we set out, as planned, soon after sunrise. We ate our cob of mealies for breakfast near the summit of the home range and then hurried through the narrow valley up towards the reclining rock figure. Even though I had tried hard to convince myself that we had only imagined the spirit figure,

I found my heart thumping and my mouth dry as we crawled through the tunnel. But on the other side, all seemed normal. The sun was high in the sky and there were no shadows on the high peak, and the whistling wind, which had sung and keened through the tunnel, was replaced by a gentle spring breeze.

We ceremoniously left our offering, our cone of confectionery balanced on the huge "knees" of the rock that looked to me like a reclining figure, and under the cardboard cone, my own little secret offering, or perhaps explanation. I had taken a small, flat stone, and copied onto it the Eland from the Bushman painting in the encyclopaedia; then I had tried to paint it with my water colours. Unlike the rabbit, I had tried very hard to make the colours as true as possible, but I was not very good at mixing colours, so they dried rather too bright and orangey. I hoped the spirit, if there were a spirit, would understand.

The climb to the high peak was shorter and easier than expected, it was almost as though a ledge had been constructed along the ridge that led around to the height of the cave. Quite near the cave the ledge widened out into a large platform below a sheer rock wall.

"Let us have our lunch here," I suggested.

I opened the rucksack and handed out sandwiches of Dinah's home-made bread with hunks of mutton, and Gran's homemade piccalilli. There was also a baked potato for each child. If it had been early winter there might have been a dried apricot, but they were all gone. We ate quickly, the brown children hardly taking their eyes from the row of cones.

These children were, I suppose, when I think about it now, quite well-fed. I remember John exclaiming how nice it was to see a plump shining brown baby, the first day back on the farm after his very brief experience of war. I realise now, having seen pictures in the war museum, how much he was disturbed by memories of wraithlike, starving babies and gaunt refugees in Europe.

The children's staple food was maize. A thick, dry lumpy porridge of mealie-meal called *n'pokotjo* for breakfast with calabash yoghurt, which I often shared because I preferred it to the dining room breakfast of chops and eggs; a stew of mealies and dried beans, sometimes with meat and vegetables for the other meals. What a nutritionist would call a diet high in complex carbohydrate. The one thing almost entirely missing from their diet was sugar. Even the ration of dark brown government sugar for each family was used almost entirely by the adults in their strong boiled coffee. So, to these children, sweets were the ultimate indulgence, rare and delicious luxuries! Their once a year Christmas box.

I was handing them out now, and each of them squealed with delight as they folded back the top and saw the chocolates inside.

"You enjoy your sweets while I go on to the cave."

Ethel protested lamely, "But we should not let you go alone. We should go with you."

She seemed to wrestle with her conscience when I assured her that it was not necessary, that I did not mind going alone, that I would only be a very little while, but in the end the chocolates and her fear of going any higher won, and she let me go. So I continued along the ledge. The rockface jutting out above my head gradually became lower and lower, so that I could no longer stand upright, but had to crawl on all fours and then worm my way on my tummy for the last few yards.

By the time I could stand again, I had moved around the curving ledge to a point from which I could no longer see the familiar mountain range to the east let alone the farmhouse. Instead I could see far to the north, the twin ranges merging, writhing, the dragon's spine disappearing into infinity. From here too, for the first time, I could see to the west of the mountains.

What I saw seemed to be some strange alien land. Flat and arid, a surrealistic landscape, with no mountain ranges, just a few flat-topped outcrops looking for all the world like abandoned ships on an endless becalmed sea. As far as I could see, there was no sign of life – no white farmhouses, no brown huts, no domesticated sheep or cattle, no wild animals; not even a bird in the sky. I felt all alone in the world.

I shuddered and turned into the cave. It had a wide entrance but it sloped back steeply. As my eyes grew accustomed to the shadows after the blinding midday sun outside, I looked up at the walls and there was a painting almost exactly like the one in the encyclopaedia.

Near the entrance were scattered stick-figure men, with bows and arrows, but so worn and corroded by the sun and the wind and the rain that they were barely visible. The animals nearest the men were also chipped and faded, but deeper in there was one Eland that was still fresh and bright. It was painted on a slight hump in the rocky cave face, and as I swayed from one foot to the other, it seemed to come alive, to thunder across distant plains. I stared at it in wonderment for a long time, marvelling at the seething strength, the sense of aliveness, and at the subtle gradation of colours.

"The exact, exact colours of a real Eland!" I found myself exclaiming aloud in admiration.

When at last I dragged my eyes from the image, when I looked down because my neck had become stiff from craning upwards for so long, something caught my eye on the floor of the cave, right at my feet. I bent to pick it up. It was only a stone, but the strangest stone I had ever seen; dark, round and smooth, with a perfectly round hole straight through the middle. I turned it around and around in my hand, caressing its contours; then I moved out into the light to see it more clearly.

Standing there, with the stone cupped in my hands I felt a new strange feeling and wondered whether it was the stone that made me feel like this. Perhaps, I thought suddenly, the spirit put it there for me, in exchange for my painted offering. Before, I had felt all alone, separate, small, insignificant, in that vast landscape. Now I felt expanded, everywhere, part of the whole world. I felt that I was the mountains, that I was the eagle that suddenly loomed above, sensuously stroking the updrafts of the wind, effortlessly hovering there.

Then, with a surge of pleasure I realised that it was a black mountain eagle, the Verreaux Eagle, the same eagle that had spiralled up towards the rising sun, on my first dawn back in the mountains. I slipped the stone into the bib of my dungarees, and lifted my arms into a great arc above my head.

As if to acknowledge my gesture the eagle sensuously, slowly banked to show me his back, emblazoned in brilliant, shimmering, sparkling, white, with a ghostly image of myself standing there with my legs apart and my arms uplifted in homage. A simple X-shaped or Y-shaped white figure on the jet black back. Then I was riding on his back, joining him in a dizzy dionysian dance of rapture, a swirling, swooping, spiralling ecstasy of aerial acrobatics. Faster and faster we tumbled and swirled and swooped until I felt quite giddy with joy; and then we were spiralling upwards, upwards, straight into the sun, merging with the sun. Suddenly I was back in my body, staring, staring, staring into the sun until I was blinded by the agonising pain of all that brightness. I buried my aching head and my burning, blinded eyes in my hands and fell to my knees.

Gradually, through the mist of that giddying black agony I remembered my friends back on the wide ledge, remembered that I had promised Ethel that I would be away for only a little while, so I stood up gingerly, opened my eyes a mere slit, and crawled back along the narrow ledge.

There seemed something strange about the ordinariness of being back in the group, all laughing and giggling, intoxicated on sweetness. I held up the stone.

"Look what I found! Isn't it beautiful? I think the Spirit left it for me on the floor of the cave!" but to my dismay the other children showed little interest.

"I saw a painting of an Eland, and an eagle too!" I exclaimed desperately trying to wrest their attention, but they were far too pre-occupied with their sweets.

They had finished their chocolates and licorice and were sucking nigger balls. They were bought as rock-hard, jet black spheres the size of large marbles, but only a few minutes sucking and they turned red or green or mauve, or yellow or white or pink. It seems that each and every nigger ball was unique in the order of the layers of colour and the depth of each layer. All the children were sucking vigorously, and then at a signal from one of them, each would pop the round ball out of the mouth and hold it aloft between two fingers. Almost invariably each had a different colour, white or green or pink or yellow, or mauve or red; but once in a while two would have the same colour, and then they would yell with delight something like the Xhosa equivalent of "Snap!"

Then back into the little round mouths would go the little round multicoloured balls.

I was handed a large black ball and joined in the game. But Ethel was nervous about being late again and soon urged us to gather up our things. I put my stone in one of the rucksacks and we set off back the way we had come.

When we reached the reclining figure rock, the offering on its knee had gone.

"Haw – the spirit took the sweets!" gasped the five brown children.

"The spirit took the offering," I repeated, then I added, casually, "Perhaps it was just a mountain baboon," but it was just something

I said, I was not at all convinced by my second suggestion. A baboon would have taken the sweets, but would it take a small, flat, painted stone?

Once more we raced down the mountainside, like a herd of frightened gazelles pursued by a lion.

I showed the round stone with a hole to the family at supper, and they were much more interested than my friends.

"I have never seen anything like it," said Gran.

"I wonder whether the hole was deliberately drilled with a flint, spun the way the Bushmen used to spin fire-sticks."

"Or maybe," suggested John, "it was a naturally weathered stone, or a meteorite fragment, and the Bushmen simply took it up to the cave because they liked the shape."

"I wonder whether it had any religious significance, like the Men-an-Tol, the stone with a hole, in Cornwall," commented one of the Aunts, turning to the other old Aunt. They had a way of taking up a topic of general conversation, and then discussing it just between the two of them, speculating, making a puzzle to solve with their rather eccentric reasoning.

"How do you know that Men-an-Tol had any religious significance?" countered the second old Aunt. "It could have had a scientific purpose, it could have been an astrological observatory."

"Or simply a work of art. Perhaps we underestimate how much the ancients delighted in beauty. Perhaps they created beautiful forms simply for the sake of beauty."

"Well I think my stone is quite beautiful," I piped in.

"Mathematically that shape is a toroid," said John, bringing the conversation back from speculation to facts.

Later I went back to the encyclopaedia to see whether there was anything about Bushman stones, but there was nothing. There was nothing about the mysterious Men-an-Tol which the Aunts had mentioned, but John's new word was there: "A toroid is a geometric form, defined as a surface described by the revolution of any closed plane curved about an axis of its own plane." Then there was something interesting, making it worth adding to my special word collection. "Some geologists and physicists suggest that the toroid shape in any solid material over a geological time period develops electromagnetic properties."

I went to bed that night, my head buzzing with strange, unknowable ideas, stroking and caressing my new stone.

However it was formed, and whatever its significance, I was entranced by that stone, it became my magic talisman. I loved to run my hands over the smooth surfaces and into the unexpected perfectly round hole, just the size of my finger.

I kept it by my pillow, the way other children would keep a favourite teddy bear or soft toy, and from that day on, always went to sleep with my hands idly caressing its contours.

CHAPTER TEN

"BE A SCULPTOR"

"Art is contemplation. It is the joy of the intelligence."

RODIN

That spring, my uncle Ben came out from England to spend a few weeks with us. When I met him I was excited, because newcomers to our distant little community were always interesting, and because by the look of him – though I could not put my finger on exactly what it was about the look of him, though perhaps it was the intense awareness of his gaze – I felt that he could be a fountain of encyclopaedic knowledge like my father. I bombarded him with questions, but he was a quiet, taciturn man, and hardly responded to my incessant chatter.

"Leave your uncle alone," said one of the Aunts. "He does not want to be pestered at this time."

I had seen the females of the family gather round and gossip about this uncle, and although they always changed the subject when I came near, because grown-ups were often secretive about some things, I gathered that he was "going through a divorce" and that, for some reason, they did not quite approve of him.

Towards the end of his visit, he wandered absently down to where we were playing with our clay oxen. He picked up one of the bulls, examined it, absentmindedly at first, and then with growing excitement, "Who made this?"

"I did," I said.

"Why, it's bloody marvellous!" exclaimed my uncle. "You have conceptualised the very essence of your subject; its energy, its vitality, its virility!"

It was the first time I had seen my uncle fired with enthusiasm about anything.

"What does that mean?" I asked.

"Well, it's easy, comparatively easy anyway, to do something realistically; it's just a matter of accurate observation and recording those observations. And it's ridiculously easy to do something totally abstract, despite the mystique the Modernists try to give it. On the other hand, to do something figurative, but to concentrate on abstract qualities like form and volume and to endow it with abstract concepts like spirit, vitality and energy – well, that is something else again!"

I did not want to ask what he meant again, so I just nodded, hoping he would go on. But he merely repeated his first observation.

"This is bloody marvellous!" and then he changed the subject. "Where did you get the clay?"

"From the donga, I mean, the riverbank," I replied.

"Can you get me some?"

So we all went down and collected a bucket of clay for him. It was a while since the last rains, and the deeply gouged donga where we collected our clay was almost dry, with only a few stagnant waterholes, so we had to gouge the clay out with our fingers and nails from between the crevasses of the rocky banks. When at last we had a bucketful, I gave it to my uncle.

"What are you going to do with it?" I asked.

"I am going to make a bust."

"You mean a woman's bosom?"

"No," said my uncle, "in sculpture, the term 'bust' means a portrait head from the chest up."

He suddenly looked at me piercingly.

"Do you know what sculpture is?"

I shook my head.

"Most people think of sculpture as those godawful statues and monuments that stand around the place! Sculpture is much more. It is creating beauty with form and volume, mass and void. It is combining strong planes with voluptuous curves, the way you did in your little bull. That is why sculpture is so much stronger than painting. Painting is purely visual. Sculpture is visual and tactile and haptic." He stopped suddenly. "I don't suppose a child like you knows what 'haptic' means?"

My eyes were shining. Uncle Ben was talking to me exactly the way I liked my father to discuss things. A mixture of new words and strange ideas, which mother called "talking above my head." I was loving every moment of it!

"Haptic," my uncle said, looking at me intently, "comes from the Greek *haptikos*, meaning 'able to lay hold of'. It is a wonderful way to explain the sheer joy one derives from some sculptures. The ability to lay hold of a small sculpture like yours, and caress it in your hands, feel it, relate to it, not just visually through the eyes, but through the hands, through one's whole body. Big sculptures can transmit haptic sensations too, when we are able to climb into them, or to press our bodies against them, respond to tactile impressions of inner bodily sensations."

By now my uncle was working with his bucket of clay, roughing out a head shape, but he went on talking.

"That is why sculpture was the pre-eminent art during the great moments of civilisation; the Greece of Pericles and Plato and Aristotle; Europe during the Renaissance, the great eras in India and Mexico. Did you know that the Athenians depicted Athena, their patron goddess, the goddess of wisdom, as a sculptor? And that Nietzsche called Apollo, the god of light and reason 'the sculptor-god'. I have a book on Greek sculpture in my case, if you would like to look at it."

I nodded and he fetched it for me.

"Now, run along, I need to concentrate."

The next day he had finished the bust. I looked at it with shining eyes.

"That is bloody marvellous!" I said cheekily, but my uncle did not seem to notice the swear-word and smiled for the first time. I walked around and around the bust. It was obviously a self-portrait, though not an exact likeness. The head was turned almost violently and looking up. From one angle it looked as though he had seen a great vision, witnessed a revelation of some great inspiration; from another angle, it looked disturbed and troubled. From a certain angle the head looked full of vitality and energy, and from yet another unsettled and restless. I could not put all this into words but I said,

"It's sort of different from each side, the expression is the same, but it seems to mean something new from each angle as you walk around it."

Uncle looked pleased. "That is another advantage of sculpture," he said. "Painting has only one viewpoint. A sculptor has 360 viewpoints and therefore he can say so much more." His voice was full of enthusiasm.

"Are you a sculptor?" I asked.

"God, no! A sculptor in our family? No, I'm a scientist. A research scientist at the university."

"Would you like to be a sculptor?" I persisted.

He thought for a long time. "I don't know," he said sadly shaking his head. "I really don't know whether I have either the guts or the talent."

"I know!" I exclaimed suddenly. "I know!" I repeated with conviction. "I am going to be a sculptor!"

Uncle knelt down and looked me straight in the eye. He grasped both my shoulders and shook them. "Good for you lass! You go for it! And don't let anyone deny your destiny!"

The next day he left.

From that moment on, I became totally obsessed with this new idea.

"I am going to be a sculptor!" I kept repeating to myself, feeling a gradual, dawning, as yet nebulous intimation that sculpture might be a way of transforming my intense, awestruck love of the mountains into something tangible.

I found myself looking at the shapes of rocks and cliffs with new eyes. Thinking of them as curves and planes, delighting in the sharp edges where the planes met.

I also revelled in the words Uncle Ben had used, like "haptic" and "mass" and "void".

Gran, my font of new words, had never used words like those. I especially loved the word "haptic". Imagine, I thought, sculpture for touching, stroking, caressing. Not something one merely stood back from, and looked at dispassionately.

"Void" took on new meaning: a space, a special kind of space made by a form around it, like my cave, or the hole in my Bushman stone.

Words are odd things. Sometimes they stop you from really seeing things, yet at other times they magically open up one's eyes to a whole new way of seeing. Now I no longer merely looked at things, I looked at the negative shapes of the spaces in and around them too.

I also thought about what Uncle Ben had said about looking at things from different angles. Three hundred and sixty different angles he had said. I tried to count them, walking around his sculpture on one plane. There were more viewpoints if one looked up at it, while lying on the ground, or stood above it, on the verandah wall, and looked down at the portrait head. I decided that large sculptures, or rock formations with hollows or caves in them could be viewed from inside the hollow, so that one could find more and more different forms and patterns.

From then on, when we climbed the mountains, I found myself not only looking, but doing too. As we wandered amongst the rocks I found myself making little rocky cairns, or circles of stones, or balancing upright boulders onto rocky outcrops.

"What are you doing?"

"Why on earth are you doing that?" asked my friends.

"I am making…" and then I ran out of words in their language, "a sort of sculpture," I finished in English.

They stared at me, uncomprehendingly.

Now, even then, as now, I have this silly need to explain myself, to justify my actions with some seemingly logical explanation. So I started telling them the story of Hansel and Gretel. How their father took them into the woods to lose them, but they dropped a trail of stones so that they could find their way back.

"If we leave a trail of standing stones like this, if we ever get lost we could follow them back!" I finished.

"No," they said solemnly, "that is not why you make these things, and besides, we know these mountains too well to ever get lost."

So for that day I went back to hunting for tortoises with them.

Then a few days later, on the very top of the home range I found myself once more collecting large, pointed stones, and trying to balance them in a circle.

"Why are you doing that ?" one of them asked again.

I did not really myself understand why I was doing it, but I dropped the stone I was holding, stood up straight, with my hands on my hips and shouted defiantly.

"I am doing it because I am doing it because I am doing it.

Because I am the way I am!

And the world is the way it is, because IT IS!

So there!" I finished in exasperation.

"Aaahh!" they chorused. "Now we understand." And all their shiny brown faces broke into wide white smiles. "Now we understand!"

Crazy, wasn't it? I did not understand, but they understood.

"We'll help! We'll all help," they shouted, so together we created a large ring of upright monoliths, right at the very top of the Mountains of the Dragon! We lugged and hauled quite big stones, all tall and pointed, some from half way down the mountain, and then had to scrape and dig little holes to make them stand upright. We finished just before dusk, a lovely time to stand back and survey our handiwork, because with the sun low in the sky one side of each stone was golden and highlighted while the other side was in deep blue-black shadow, and each cast a strange shadow on the rocks below.

"The sun is low in the sky," reminded Ethel, and though we were on the home range the others started bounding down the mountainside immediately. I followed, though I longed to linger, to see our circle in that strange translucent, shadowless light of the brief African twilight.

Because by this time I had discovered something that Uncle Ben had not mentioned and that was light! How a sculpture or form could subtly change as the light of the sun changed, and then could almost totally change as the light of the sun gave way to the eerie light of the moon!

In the phantom light of the moon ordinary things, simple things, pieces of rusty old farm machinery, or cairns of rocks, turned into eerily beautiful sculptures. The expression on the face of Uncle Ben's sculpture which he had left abandoned in the corner of the verandah, changed all the time, in the moonlight, in the sunlight, at different times of the day.

I found myself noticing how brilliant sunlight and dark shadowed patterns could transform a shape; and then there was the magic of backlighting, the way the early morning sun burnished a bright golden outline around a dark silhouette.

In the searing midday sun the marble girl in the graveyard was all glistening white highlights against deep black undercuts, strong, indomitable, striding joyously into the wind, full of some strange confident joie de vivre, bursting with spirit electricity; yet in the evening light all that energy seemed to dematerialise, to turn ghostly and wistfully sad, a haunting shadow-spirit hovering overhead.

Then the discovery of a group of our clay oxen silhouetted against the dawn sun, which outlined each and every bull in a thin halo of gold, and threw weird and wonderful shadow patterns onto the flat bare earth below them.

I experimented with light on my Bushman stone. At first I had thought of it as a tactile object, something to hold and feel and caress in the dark. Now I saw it as visual, as a pure simple form that had the powers of transformation in changing light. I always took a candle to my room, when I went to bed, and one night I noticed how moving the candle seemed to change the stone. Lit from the side the hole in the stone became a pool of blackness, an infinitely bleak, black void. But with the candle behind it the space became a tunnel of light and hope.

As I moved the candle around, up, down, around and around, the rings of light and shadow flitted around the solid form in an infinite variety of tonal patterns.

Sunlight does not alter paintings one iota, I thought, they just stay the same. Gran had several paintings, both originals and prints lining the walls of the long corridor. She seemed to like literary paintings, allegories, paintings that had an authenticity of soul, or that had meaning and a message. There were several Pre-Raphaelite prints, but I decided that her favourite artist must be G.F. Watts, because there were three of his works, including a print called *Hope of the World**, a dejected, blindfolded figure with a harp, sitting on the globe of the world. She looks hopeless rather than hopeful, I thought to myself. And was all that meaning necessary in a work of art? My Bushman stone could take on as much mystery and meaning just in a simple, formal shape.

"I think I prefer sculpture," I ventured one day, standing in front of the Watts print. "This figure is very beautiful, but she has the same expression, day in and day out, in daylight and candlelight, not like..." then I had to bite my tongue, because Gran did not know of my secret visits to the graveyard. I had been going to say, "Not like the sculpture in the graveyard; she is in a different mood every time I visit her, every time I see her from a slightly different angle, or in different light, with shadows in different places and in different tones."

Gran did not seem to notice my biting of my tongue and went on, "Then one day, if you ever go to the very southern tip of Africa you must climb the steep side of Devil's Peak, above the University, and you will find a sculpture called *Physical Energy†* which is also by Watts, in front of the Rhodes Memorial."

"See that wonderful rock formation that looks like a reclining figure," I thought to myself, the next time I looked across to the far

* To view image, go to Google images: Hope Watts.
† To view image, go to Google images: Watts Physical Energy.

range. "One day I am going to make a huge sculpture, just like that! Perhaps it will stand in one of those flat parks. Then all those poor city people who have never climbed mountains will have some idea of what my craggy, rugged mountains are like.

"I will make it gigantic, with caves under the knees, so that little city children who have never explored caves can climb into it and feel what it is like to shelter in a cave, feel some of the magic I felt in my cave."

I grew more and more excited as I climbed onto the giant's knees and shouted across the valley, at the cliff-face with the cave in it.

"I am going to be a sculptor!"

And the mountains (or was it the spirit of the little people?) echoed back again and again.

"Be a sculptor!

Be a sculptor!

Be a sculptor!"

I called out again, "I have an unbearable yearning to be a sculptor!"

This time the answer seemed to resonate from the very soul of the universe.

"Be a sculptor!

Be a sculptor!

Be a sculptor!"

I can still remember feeling a welling, surging, joyous conviction, being ecstatically confident that if I wanted something badly enough the whole universe would conspire to help me.

But happiness of such overwhelming intensity is rare and fragile, and doomed to be shattered, because it is only in early childhood that we have the supreme confidence to believe that we have the freedom, the emotional freedom, to choose our own destinies.

CHAPTER ELEVEN

SEPARATION

"This is the spirit Beauty must induce,

Wonderment and delicious trouble, longing and love

and a trembling that is all delight."

PLOTINUS

When I came down from the mountain, there was another visitor.

"Meet my friend, Mr Van der Poste. He is an archeologist," said my step-grandfather. "He was very interested when I told him about the cave you found. He wants you to take him there in the morning."

The archaeologist was an interesting companion, and he told me how he was trying to re-create the history of the Bushmen from the string of cave paintings across the continent.

He also had something to say about the geology of the mountains themselves. "These are some of the oldest mountains in the world," he said. "The Himalayas and Andes and Alps are geological youngsters compared with these wise and wrinkled ancients."

Before we set out he spent a long time talking to the Old Grandfather of my friends.

"It is so isolated up here," he said to me as we climbed, "that there are still Bushmen descendants among the natives. In fact the man you call the 'Old Grandfather' tells me his mother was a Bushman and his wife was also half-Bushman. The other old couple who moved here recently are also Bushmen."

I had not really thought about it, but now I realised that these people were much smaller and a lovely apricot brown, lighter than most of the others; and that his grandchildren were also smaller and had a very distinctive body shape, the swinging backs and swelling buttocks of the Bushman painting.

"Those enormous behinds were essential for their survival," he said when I mentioned it.

"There were times of plenty, but other times when game was scarce and there was no food for days or even weeks. Only those who had stored reserves survived, and the Bushmen can store reserves of fat and protein in those very prominent behinds. There is even a scientific name for them, 'steatopygia'."

"All the girls here, Xhosas too, think that a huge bottom is a thing of great beauty," I told him.

"I know," he said.

"And they tell me I will never find a husband because I have no tail!"

He laughed.

"They are beautiful though," I went on, "their behinds I mean. If you think of them as form and volume and mass and contour." I was trying to remember all the words Uncle Ben had used. "The whole body is a beautiful form."

He was climbing ahead of me and only grunted.

"My friends are so lucky," I chatted on, "they have good skins so they don't wear clothes most of the year. They can enjoy the feel of the wind and the sun and raindrops on their skin."

"Yes, he conceded, "but the first thing the missionaries do everywhere, whenever they go out to help indigenous people, to civilise them, is to give them clothes to cover their nakedness."

"Do you think wearing clothes is a sign of civilisation?" I asked him.

He was struggling to haul himself up a sheer rock face that I had scrambled up like a baboon on all fours. When at last he was standing besides me on the ledge, he turned the question back at me,

"What do you think?"

"Well my Uncle Ben thinks that Ancient Greece was a great civilisation, and they competed naked in the Olympic Games. He lent me a book of Greek statues, and they are almost all nudes, even the goddesses, and they are also very beautiful. You know I think the human body is almost as beautiful as these wonderful mountains." I did not tell him that since looking at Uncle Ben's book I had been looking intensely at my friends' bodies.

From that point on we had to go single file along the ledge and could not talk any more. Mr Van der Poste found it very difficult to negotiate the last section, where we had to squirm flat on our tummies, wriggling forward like snakes, between low overhanging rocks above us, and the narrow ledge that dropped away to a sheer fall below us. For a while I thought he would never make it, that the space was just too small for a grown man to squeeze through. Fortunately he was a rather skinny grown man, and so after a last squirming wriggling effort we reached the cave.

At first he seemed disappointed at the poor condition of the figures, and then like me, he became very excited at the sense of power in
the one Eland deep inside the cave. He took several photographs of the
painting, spraying it with a little distilled water, which he had brought
with him, to make it show more clearly. Now the polychrome painting
showed even more clearly the subtle shading of the colours, the merging and blending of the whites and pinks and reddish browns.

"Such a clever artist!" I murmured.

"Yes," he replied, "some of these painters had an uncanny genius
for representing natural animal poses or movements that reveal in the
simplest way the whole nature of the animal."

Then he wrote for a while into his little notebook while I gazed,
spellbound once more, at the lovely painting of the Eland.

When he had finished writing, he flicked back a few pages in his
notebook, and pointed out to me a sketch he had made. It was labelled
in his neat writing, "Portraits of Bushwomen from a rockshelter near
Elliot."

"Look," he said. "This is what you were talking about earlier. These
three women all have tiny heads, short arms, pendulous little breasts,
but just look at their magnificent behinds. And strong, shapely legs
for running vast distances! Let us take a closer look at the figures here
now."

There was a group of little running figures near the entrance to
the cave, almost invisible under a patina of age and dust, and hidden in a shadow under a projecting rock at that time of day. However,
when sprayed with the distilled water they miraculously cleared, and
we could discern seven figures, all running, leaping, hurdling, chasing
game. They were thin as sticks, but all of them had beautiful bottoms.

"See, here too, your little Bushman artist so admired that *steatopygia* that he emphasised it in all his painting. It was the most distinctive feature of these people."

Staring at these little figures, as they slowly disappeared from view, as they slowly dried and merged with the rock-face again, I felt a surge of inexplicable elation, a feeling of being suffused with awe and admiration for whatever it was, or whoever it was, who had designed these little people. Gran seldom used the word God, she was more likely to say Mother Nature or The Creator. Well, I thought to myself, the Creator, seeing the need in these people, could easily have lumped them with a hump on the back like a camel, or given them fat stomachs or thick legs, but instead, he designed for them exquisitely rounded curving behinds as storage space for extra life energy.

Truly, I smiled to myself, the Creator must be a sculptor at heart, like Uncle Ben's Greek sculptor-god, Apollo.

And what a delight to that Creator to see how much these little people appreciated the beauty of His handiwork.

On the way down the mountains, Mr van der Poste asked me if I knew the names of the plants. I told him a few, saying their clicking native names.

"That is interesting," he commented. "It seems to me that some words in this region are mere clicks of the tongue, especially words for local plants and animals. You see, they are identical to the tongue-clicking words of the Bushman of the Kalahari and quite different from the Zulu words for the same plants used only a little to the north of here."

I was surprised that the language I had learned was only spoken up here, in these sparsely populated and isolated mountains, and not by all the natives of Africa.

At dinner that evening, a special evening meal for the visitor because we had been out all day, Gran asked,

"Have you shown Mr Van der Poste your Bushman stone?"

For some reason I could not explain, I had been secretive about the stone, and had avoided mentioning it to the archaeologist. But now I had no alternative.

I fetched it from my bed. The man seemed very interested, turning it over in his hands.

Then speaking directly to my step-grandfather, turning in his direction, away from me, this man who had all day talked to me as though I were an adult, as though my opinion counted, who had laughed with me, wondered with me, so that I thought he was my friend, said,

"May I keep this for my museum?"

"No! No!" I cried,

"No, that is my stone!"

My step-grandfather had been carving a leg of mutton on a flat silver tray. He held up the elaborate silver carving knife for a moment, almost as if to cut off my cry, and then put it down on the tray, and half-bowed to the man.

"Of course, by all means, you must have it."

Those words are indelibly etched on my mind:

"Of course, by all means, you must have it."

Then he looked at me.

"You must not be so selfish. In the museum, everybody can see the stone."

I was beside myself with horror and grief. My precious stone was not meant to sit in a glass case. It was meant to be loved and caressed.

I burst into tears.

"Go to your room until you can control yourself," said Gran sternly, and instead of taking my side, which I expected her to do, she proceeded to apologise profusely to the man for my rudeness and selfishness.

"I can't think what has come over her. She didn't make a fuss like this when we sent her pet baboon to the zoo. She didn't even cry like this when her dog died."

I could easily explain why I did not cry when people expected me to. The orphaned baboon Gran mentioned, had, as he grew bigger, taken to pinching me. I could not decide whether this was a sign of malice or of affection, baboon affection; but I knew that I had become afraid of him, and greeted the news that he was going with more relief than grief.

My dog had been a very different matter; a bouncy, barky, little fox terrier called Foxie, full of life and vitality. One day there was a cry of anguish from one of the servants, and we rushed to see what the commotion was about. There, in a little walled garden, was Foxie, stiff and bloated. "Puff adder!" cried Dinah. I was stunned, beyond speaking, beyond crying. Stunned by the harsh reality of death, and the truth that snakes did bite, and that they were poisonous. Things I had been told, things I had known in the abstract; but never really feared before.

Perhaps it is easier to explain why one does not cry, than why one does.

I still find it difficult to explain why I was so deeply miserable, so utterly bereft at the loss of my beloved stone. Why it seemed to me that I had lost more than just a stone, more than just a magic talisman, that a gift of the spirit, a gift of certitude, had been withdrawn.

CHAPTER TWELVE

SEVERANCE

"The most beautiful thing we can experience

is the mysterious. It is the true source

of all art and science."

ALBERT EINSTEIN

A few days after the loss of my stone, while I was still in uncom-prehending mourning for my stone, Gran said, "Your mother and father are coming to fetch you soon."

"No, no!" I protested. "Let me stay. Just a little longer. Please, please, Gran."

But Gran, my beloved Gran, my ally and comforter, hardened her face. "No," she said. "The time has come. This time you must go."

When my parents arrived they we seemed eager to assess my

progress. Father in particular was eager to assess his own assertion that I would make more progress under Gran's tuition than at school. So I read to him. I showed him the stars, and named the galaxies and the planets. (Up here in the crystal clear, high mountain air you could almost reach up and grasp the stars.)

"I even learned a science word, an anatomy word, that I bet you don't know," I exclaimed boastingly, buoyed up by the fact that he seemed impressed by my astronomical observations.

"*Steatopygia!* It means 'a beautiful rounded, sticking out behind!'"

My father threw his head back and roared with laughter, "See my darling," he turned to my mother. "They never would have taught her such a big word at Miss Pinkerton's school now would they?"

"It really is a scientific word," I stammered, wondering why he was laughing so much.

"Oh yes," he agreed, "I can even explain it to you. *Steato* is Greek for 'fat,' and *pyge* means 'buttocks'. So literally it means 'fat buttocks!'"

I did not think that sounded nearly as nice as my definition, but he was going on, "That Greek word *steato* is also the root of the geological word 'steatite' for a kind of talcstone. I used to wonder why a stone should be called fat, until I found that it has a slightly greasy feeling. Artists sometimes carve it because it is much softer than marble and they call it soapstone."

I loved the way my father seemed to love words and the way they are formed, and I was also heartened that he should mention carving because later I wanted to show him my bull, and perhaps talk about the things that Uncle Ben had talked about, and introduce some of the words my uncle had introduced me to, but in the meantime it seemed safer to show him the scrap-book with wild flowers that Kay had taught me to press between sheets of blotting paper, with notations describing where they grew and what the plant was like. I had found out a few of their English names and had written them underneath. I knew many of their native names and said the clicking sounds, which were impossible to write. Father who seemed to enjoy showing off his Greek and Latin supplied the pressed flowers from Gran's garden with Latin botanical names.

I showed him a little book I had made that I had named "Calender of Seasons of Fruits". I had been amazed that Gran could predict that "next month is Mulberry month".

"How does each tree know its time?" I had countered. I wanted to check whether it really was the same every year. It was also fun to know what to look forward to, to drool in anticipation. These days in England, with cold storage and importing, some things are beginning to be available for most of the year, which takes all the fun, all the delicious, craving anticipation out of seasonal delights.

I began my book with mulberries, the first fruit of the season, coming long after the dried apricots and dried figs were gone, and every-one was desperately longing for the taste of fruit, because we had had no fruit for months. There was a massive mulberry tree at the end of Gran's garden, its trunk gnarled and knotted, so old that it might have been planted by that great-grandfather and great-grandmother under the marble flowergirl, and two more mulberry trees, cuttings from the old one, in the orchard. When the berries ripened we all swarmed, almost all day, through the trees, stuffing the juicy black berries into our mouths, getting covered in berry juice as we climbed. It was not so obvious on my brown friends, but I came down by the end of the day, black and blue all over. During the mulberry season I refused to eat anything else; why waste tummy space on meat and potatoes that were there all the year round I insisted, when there were such delicious berries to be devoured? Yet despite our stoutest efforts, we could not eat them all, so Gran sent us up with baskets, and when we had filled them all she made mulberry jam. After the mulberries there was a short break, and then came the strawberries, just as delicious, with sugar and fresh cream, but not nearly as prolific.

Then the apricots. There were more apricot trees than any other fruits, and my step-grandfather used to boast that there was something about the soil or the minerals in the bore-water, or the high mountain climate that helped him produce the best apricots in the whole wide world! Once in a while there would be a late frost, when the trees were covered in blossom, and then there would be no fruit that year at all, but when there was, the apricots surpassed even Grandfather's boasting. Ethel and Iris and I could not wait for them to ripen, and so, even though we were told not to, we would sneak down to the orchard and pick some, still yellow-green, and eat them; and then suffer terrible tummy aches. But once they had ripened, turned that wonderful glowing golden-pink, my favourite colour, the same glowing golden pink of the sunrise, then I could eat them all day, like the mulberries. This time, when we were sent out to gather baskets full, Gran did not make jam but dried the apricots, and stored them away for the winter. After the apricots, fruits and vegetables came on thick and fast. Peaches, nectarines, tomatoes, watermelons, grapes and figs. With the grapes and figs came flocks of birds, so that several little boys were hired to play amongst the vines and fig trees all day. Half were supplied with tins full of stones to rattle and shake, while the others were given saucepan lids to clang together like cymbals whenever the birds descended.

My book of fruits was only a little book, but detailed the blossoming and fruiting of each variety, with little drawings of each, and it seemed to please Father.

The very best, the offering I hoped would please him most, I saved for last. I went to fetch it.

Now one of the most disarming things about my father is that, when he is interested, he gives an individual his full and undivided attention. While he was testing me, he had given me his full attention, but now he was engrossed and concentrating on a political discussion with his step-father-in-law.

When I returned with my sculptured bull in my hands and proudly proffered it for his assessment, he gave it a mere cursory glance.

"No," he said. "That is not very good. Your sense of observation has deserted you there," and he returned to his political argument.

I was devastated. "Can't you see?" I wanted to protest. "I was not trying to observe and record. I did not want to show only what a bull LOOKS like. I wanted to distil its essence."

What were the words Uncle had used? "Give it a sense of vitality and virility."

It was no use; Father was not in the least interested. At least he had been pleased with my other achievements, I thought with a sigh. I had become very eager to please.

Mother had been so hard to please. The first thing she had noticed was my hair.

"What has happened to your long hair?" she exclaimed. When she had left I had had long hair, but even though Gran tied it back with satin ribbons it was so silky and slithery that before I was half-way up the mountain it would be blowing in my eyes and getting tangled in the bushes. I envied my companions their head-hugging little tufts. Kay's eyes had lit up when I mentioned this. She loved cutting hair but could seldom find a willing victim.

"There! An Eton crop!" she exclaimed after prolonged snipping. Although I missed the feeling of my long hair being brushed a hundred strokes every night, on the mountains my new haircut made me feel light-headed and free.

Mother had seemed even more displeased with my hands.

Climbing rocky mountains is not done upright on two feet. It is better done on all fours, like a mountain baboon. At first my hands had become raw and grazed from climbing, but Nature, in her wisdom, soon compensates for natural stresses. I had noticed that my native companions never wore shoes and they could walk over prickly bushes or jagged rocks with impunity. Nature had compensated them with thick, leathery, almost horny soles to their feet. After a few months, the heels of my hands had developed similar thick leathery pads, that protected the soft flesh underneath. The backs of my hands, that at first had burnt bright pink in that unfiltered mountain sunlight, had developed a brown, flaky, protective layer, and the nails were ragged and torn from gouging clay from the cliffs and crevasses.

Despite all this I liked my hands. My long fingers seemed strong and efficient and full of life. I could not understand why my mother made such a fuss.

As the time for me to leave grew closer, Ethel and Iris became more and more miserable, and I found myself basking in their misery, in their sympathy for me. I lamented my fate, exaggerating the dreadful place I was going back to, where it was cold and wet and dark and smoggy all the time (as it had seemed for the months I had been in London). I reminded them how snooty the people were in this place I was going to, how lacking in humour, so that they did not even laugh at our funny stories.

Ethel and Iris looked at me with eyes brimming with tears. "And when you have gone, what will happen to us?"

"Oh YOU are the lucky ones, you will still have the sun and the sky and the mountains..." And then, for the first time, I comprehended that the tears were for themselves, not for me.

I stared at them, disoriented, thrown from my self-centred fulcrum by a shift of focus in my perception, the way a film changes from one camera, focusing, close-up, on the face of the heroine, to another camera, wide angled, from another viewpoint, to other characters.

I saw, looking from their perspective, how much my going would alter their lives. While I was there they led privileged lives; they had the run of the house, they ate what I ate. They came in the car with us to the little outpost, or to visit neighbouring farms. They came on the occasional trips to the nearest big town, and even stayed overnight in my hotel room. When the hotel man started to protest Gran said they were my maids, and I could not do without them, and if I awoke alone in the room I would scream and wake all the guests, so the man said it would be alright as long as they slept on the floor. And Gran and I smiled our consent, because we knew that the girls would have slept on the floor anyhow, as they always did in their own hut. Ethel and Iris loved the town, loved its ice-cream parlour with seven different flavours of ice cream; but I did not like it at all.

That big town was spoiled for me by a seemingly brief incident. We had been to a concert in the Town Hall, the local orchestra had performed a program of Mozart, and we were walking back, late at night, the very short distance to our hotel. Suddenly in the dark there loomed in front of us a man, a native man, lying on the pavement, grumbling and groaning.

"Quick!" I exclaimed. "He is sick, we must get help."

"No," said my step-grandfather. "He is drunk."

"Then we must call his friends or his family to take him home," I suggested.

"He probably has no family and no home in this town."

"Well, perhaps we should call the police," I was desperate.

"The gaols would be overflowing if the police picked up every drunk in this town," said my step-grandfather.

"Well, can we then just sit down and talk to him?" I asked, squatting down on my haunches next to the man. "*Molo,*" I said. "Hello."

He did not respond but just went on muttering gibberish.

"Come away, there is nothing we can do. Absolutely nothing we can do," said my Gran taking my hand and dragging me away.

In bed that night, instead of memories of the music filling my mind, the image of the man filled my mind, and I could not sleep in the soft hotel bed, I could not fall asleep until I lay down on the floor next to Ethel and Iris. It was not that he was drunk that worried me, the natives drank plenty of kaffir beer on the farm, it was the way people, even his own native people, did not seem to care. Even my grandmother who had always seemed to care so much for every single one on the farm from the oldest man to the tiniest piccaninny, seemed to have lost some of her caring.

Next morning we drove past the place, on our way home, and there was no sign of the drunken man, the street was pristine clean, a native man was hosing the sandstone paving, and a native maid was sweeping the water into the gutter, but still the memory made me hate the town, hate the brutal awareness of my ignorance of what lay behind its slick facade of plate-glass shop windows and elaborate sandstone civic buildings. I recoiled at that first inkling that the quiet harmony and sense of community on the sparsely populated farm (perhaps because it was sparsely populated) was not a reflection of the universal human condition.

But Ethel and Iris relished the trips to town, they loved to boast to the others when we got back about the ice creams they had tasted at the ice-cream parlour.

They also loved to tell the others, endlessly, about the sea, the great waters that grab you. They had been with us to the sea, to a little settlement called Morgan Bay on the Wild Coast, and stayed, once more, in my hotel room. They came to the beach with us, but would not swim in the sea which terrified them; and when the fishermen caught a huge man-eating shark, right there in the river mouth, they saw it as a further vindication of their position. They joined in our long beach walks, and our hunt for shells, but when I joined the other children in organised games, they would melt away, murmuring something about going to collect bottles for seawater. They did not eat with us in the dining room, but in the kitchen with the hotel maids, and I had accepted this as one of the rules of the hotel.

When we returned to the farm they insisted on taking bottles and bottles of magic medicinal sea water back for everyone; brown beer bottles labelled Lion Lager and white whisky bottles labelled Black Douglas, but all filled with salty sea-water, and a little sand. So many that my grandfather teased them and said the car would never make it up the steep mountain passes, and that they would have to get out and push if they wanted to take home all those bottles.

I saw now, for the first time that Ethel and Iris enjoyed being privileged, they enjoyed being the only natives on the farm ever to have seen the sea. They enjoyed being responsible for me, being my minders, having a purpose in life. Without me, there was no place for them in the house, their importance evaporated, they were too young to be maids or inside girls, too old to be tied to their mother's apron-strings in the kitchen. Back in the kraal, they would be too old for the little children's games, but much too young to look for husbands yet.

I did not know what to say, so I put on a show of bravado.

"Don't worry, I'll soon be back! I will soon think of some scheme. I will make a plan. Look how I came back to you last time."

And, in a show of faith in me that made me feel self-centred again, they smiled through their tears and nodded vigorously, "Yes, yes! You will make a plan!"

"You are very smart, you will make a plan."

They were sure that I would make a plan, that I could find a way; but when I looked inside myself I sensed with a sinking heart that perhaps I was deceiving them, that perhaps I was lying. How could I possibly make a plan powerful enough to pit against the power of grown-ups, the power of fate?

Angry with myself, not wanting to endure those black, liquid, trusting eyes on me, on my deception, I said brusquely to them,

"You must go home now. I will walk with you, half-way."

"It is not necessary," said Ethel primly, hurt by my brusqueness, but I strode out into the backyard, and they followed.

A full moon was floating across the sky, above a black and silver world, and the silence was like crystal.

Exactly halfway to the huts I halted and turned around to face the girls.

"Did you hear that?" I whispered.

"What was that?" they whispered, simultaneously.

An agonising howl, a cry of great misery, not loud, but infinitely miserable, quavered through the crystal-still night.

"Did you hear that?" intoned a fourth voice, near to us, unseen in the darkness; a voice so deeply bass, so low-toned that it was barely audible to the human ear, but a voice resonant with the power of knowing.

"It is the call of the mountain leopardess. She is alone, the last one in this mountain. So she calls to the Moon."

It was the voice of the Old Grandfather, and now we could see his grizzled, wrinkly hair and beard, silver in the moonlight.

The call of the lonely leopard reverberated through the crystal silence of the night, shattering it into splinters that cut deep into my heart. I sensed, deep down inside me a response, a howl of agony, a cry of misery that rose and filled my throat, strained at my vocal cords until they ached with tension; but before I could open my mouth to let it out, before I had uttered the slightest sound, I felt the bony, leathery finger of the Old Grandfather pressing my lips.

"Better not," he whispered, in his language. "Better not that she should hope. Better that she should call only to her sister, the Moon."

There was one more excruciatingly sad, agonised cry, that subsided into a whimpering mewing.

Then silence.

The Moon stood still, high in the black sky. She did not answer her sister, the mountain-leopard. She stopped still and silent. We all stood, statue-still, and silent, in her crystal-cold light.

I could not utter a sound, my throat still filled with the severed cry, the cry blocked by the old man's finger; distended yet constricted, full yet quite empty. When the silence became unbearable I turned and ran, leopard silent, leopard lithe, leopard miserable, back to the house. The kitchen was almost dark, lit only by one candle, darker than the silvery moonlight outside, so that, as I turned around in the doorway I could see quite clearly, in the phantom light of the moon, the silver-haired old man with my friends, holding their hands, leading them away from me, up the mountainside to the huts.

The next day we left. It was necessary to set out before dawn for the long car trip to the nearest railway station. Although it was barely light when we came out to the car, there was a long line of people, children and adults, waiting to bid me farewell.

I walked slowly up the line, with my parents behind me, shaking each hand, like the Queen inspecting the troops.

"Goodbye, goodbye," I said to the first few, in their language.

"I will see you again."

"I will be back."

"It is good that you will come back," they said.

"It is right that we shall see you here again."

"Yes, I will see you again."

"I will be back," I repeated.

I turned around, and as if to confirm it to them, I said to Father in English, "I will come back to visit, won't I?"

"No," said Father flatly. "No. Your grandparents are selling out here, and going to New Zealand."

"No!" I gasped, and ran to Gran.

"Gran!" I cried. "Say that is not true."

But Gran, my beloved ally, my protector and comforter, who had betrayed me twice in the last few weeks, denied me a third time.

She said nothing, but her face said it for her.

I felt the blood draining from my face, my face turning cold, blood-less white, and my pupils dilate, until my eyes felt like black holes of pain. Slowly I turned around and looked at the row of black faces.

They were still, silent, a row of black granite statues, in the grey pre-dawn light, but their eyes spoke for them.

Their eyes were like black pits of sorrow.

"You will not be back."

"You will not come again."

"We will not, ever, see you again!"

I could not bear to look at those eyes, especially the eyes of Iris and Ethel, their limpid brown eyes turned black and empty, like black pits, so I lifted my gaze to the shadowy mountains. At that moment, the sun struck the topmost granite spires a dazzling, brilliant gold.

Then I was running. Running as fast as my legs would go. Running with all my might. Running towards the mountains. Nothing would take me from them.

Let all the others go to New Zealand, wherever that might be, to England. I would live in my cave, a true child of the mountains. If the Bushmen could survive up there, so could I with the help of my friends!

I ran like the wind, surging with the strength of resolution, and as I ran, the pounding of my heart was louder than the pounding of my feet.

Then I was aware that there was another set of pounding foot-beats and Father's hand grasped my shoulder like a clamp and spun me around to face the house and car and the row of people.

Suddenly, that last little spark of defiance drained from me. I felt myself turning cold, lifeless, stiff, as I was marched, stiff as a robot, back to the car. I caught a glimpse of a reflection in the shiny black car; a white ghostlike apparition, with a ragged white urchin-cut, in a white dress. Only its eyes burned, like black holes of agony in that gaunt, white face.

Father opened the back door and I climbed in, mechanically, beside Mother. Father sprinted around to the front passenger seat and leapt in beside my step-grandfather who already had the engine run-ning, ready to take off.

I knelt on the back seat and looked out of the back window. The row of black faces, and the one white face of my grandmother had turned gaunt and grotesque, like masks, like death masks, and all of them had black holes of agony where their eyes should have been.

The pain in my heart told me that I would never see them again.

With the car speeding and jolting to catch the train, the faces soon disappeared from sight.

I raised my eyes to the mountain peaks. They took longer to disappear but when they did, I realised with utter finality, the way one somehow knows these things, that I would never, ever, see them again.

CHAPTER THIRTEEN

THE SOUL OF THE UNIVERSE

"The greatest danger
for most of us
is not that our aim is
too high and we miss it,
but that it is too low
and we reach it."

MICHELANGELO

When we arrived back in England, I discovered that Mother and Father had moved house just before they had come to fetch me; from the city to a town to the south of London where they said the air was less likely to give me asthma. It worked, because I only had a few mild attacks this time, though I had a cold for most of the first winter.

The air did Mother good too. At first I noticed that she was even more delicate and highly strung than I remembered. Once I asked her if perhaps she smoked too many cigarettes.

"No," she countered, "smoking is good for me, it calms me, settles my nerves."

So it seemed did the medicinal gin and tonic at sundown every evening. She must have been right, in the films I see, if anyone is stressed someone always lights them a cigarette or pours them a drink.

I sometimes feel guilty that I do not understand my mother very well, she keeps her feelings so well hidden.

I understood, just a little, on the train trip across Africa. From the station where my step-grandfather dropped us, the two steam engines chuffed and choked west over the mountains, and then across endless, semi-desert plains. The trip seemed as endless as the plains and in my memory it seemed as if for days I sat huddled up next to the window, hugging my misery to me, immersed in my own grey gloom. Yet even through the mists of misery, I registered that whenever I glanced at my mother, if at the same time she glanced up from the magazine that she held in front of her face, her eyes would widen with a kind of blind, mindless terror.

At last my father noticed too, and asked what was troubling her.

"Trains terrify me!" she almost sobbed.

I had wondered why she had seemed reluctant when my father said he would like to see the interior, travel overland to Cape Town, rather than drive down to the Indian Ocean to catch the ship; the way they had come, and the way my mother had taken me back the first time.

Now she continued, in a tight stilted voice, "I travelled this train to boarding school in Cape Town. They sent me off when I was still quite small. The first time my mother came with me, and the first holidays a teacher going in the same direction escorted me most of the way back. But after that my mother was too busy with the younger children, so I was sent alone, until two years later when my sister came with me, when I was responsible for her.

"They put me in a first class compartment, and told me to lock the door, that the guard would come and check me now and then. I did not know which was more terrifying, the endless hours alone, or the booming voice of the guard rattling his key in my door. They gave me money to go and have my meals in the dining car, but I could not bear the thought of sitting there at a table all alone, ordering from the supercilious waiter, with everyone staring at me. Besides, I was far too frightened to cross from carriage to carriage on the speeding train. But the terror of the train was nothing compared with the station where we change trains!"

She stopped suddenly and changed the subject. I wondered what it was about the station that had worried her so much that even now she could not bring herself to talk about it. Especially as we were fast approaching that station where we had to change trains, where we had to wait, as she had had to wait, five hours before our connecting train from the north, going south, came through.

The station was a junction right in the middle of nowhere. On the railway map that my father found it was like the centre of a spoked wheel. As if some imperial railway builder, in the nineteenth century, imagining that his railways would take the light of his civilisation into the darkest outreaches of the dark continent, had drawn a main line from Cape to Cairo, then arbitrarily put his pen on that spot for the lines from the north-west, the south-west, the north-east and south-east to join the main line from the south and the north. The centre of this spoked wheel was right in the middle of nowhere, right in the middle of the Great Karroo Desert.

I felt too a sense of strangeness at that station, and even my
father seemed determined to get my mother out of there as quickly
as possible as he, all brisk efficiency, found a porter, asked the station
master if there was a hotel, and bustled us along. On the surface it was
all a labyrinth world of railway lines, and rail trucks, goods trains filled
with cattle, farm machinery, iron ore and coal; oil tanks, and closed
goods vans, and a few passenger carriages, some being shunted and
shoved backwards and forwards, from line to line by huffing, puffing
steam engines. It was a world not of people, but of machinery and engines, many old, cold dead; every engine that had ever come to Africa
seemed to be waiting, brooding, or abandoned here. Father guided us
unerringly from platform to platform, and then held our hands as we
crossed several lines, out through the guarded gate, into a wide, dusty,
deserted street.

The town, bypassed by major roads, was small and old, a ghost
town appendage to that vast metaphysical station where nothing and
no one arrived, and from which nothing and nobody departed. Everything and everyone was transitory, temporarily suspended, seemingly
abandoned, but ultimately in transit. We seemed to be the only ones
abandoned there at that time that day, three lonely stick figures, as we
crossed the road to the old Station Hotel, and took a room so that we
could change out of our sooty train clothes. Across the mountains, and
across the hot, still, suspended desert, the billowing black coal smoke
from the two engines had every now and then descended onto the trail-
ing carriages behind, so we felt hot and grimy.

We all had a bath, a very shallow bath because the brackish bore
water trickled so slowly out of the taps, my father at one end of the
passage in the gents, and my mother and I at the other end, in the
green-tiled ladies. Our room was the only one occupied.

All cleaned and spruced up, Father took us down to the lounge, a brown room, with brown panelled walls and brown furniture, and a musty brown smell, and ordered a beer for himself, a lemonade for me and a gin-and-tonic for my mother. We were the only ones in the lounge, though I could hear a few guttural voices coming from the men's bar, and though my father talked cheerfully I could see the abandoned atmosphere of the old room unsettle my mother, make her nervous again, make her say, several times, perhaps we should be going, perhaps we will miss our train.

So, with half an hour to wait, we went back to the station. In that quivering gloom of the brief African dusk, the station seemed to have changed; the labyrinth that had seemed to have some vestige of order in the afternoon was now all chaos, carriages abandoned at all angles, each seeming to conceal some dark enigmatic secret. The station master was nowhere to be seen, perhaps having his supper, and there was not a single porter to be found. Even my father, usually unerring in his sense of direction, had to backtrack, seemed to lose his way, before we found the right platform, and sat down on the little backless bench. There was not another soul on our platform, though there were little huddles of natives, standing close together, silently, on the platform across the track behind us. Nearby some cattle, in the cattle-trucks lowed forlornly, and in the distance there was still some desultory shunting going on, one could hear the distant clanging of the coupling and the clanking of the uncoupling. An electric light, a weak, ineffective bare lightbulb went on just as total darkness descended, just as we heard the rushing, roaring of an approaching train. It did not stop or slow, hurtling straight at us, black as night, no lights at all except the glowing red furnace in the belly of the engine, and as it passed its heat swept us like a blast from hell, followed by the closed boxes of the goods vans, black as coffins, clicketty clack, clicketty clack, clicketty clicketty clack, on and on, endless dozens of them.

My mother's beautiful big eyes were wide with terror in the reflected firelight. "What if our train has already gone? What if I have to spend the whole night on this terrible station? What if the next train that stops at this platform is the wrong one? What if I get onto it and it carries me away to the remotest, wildest reaches of Africa?" Her voice was strangled, barely audible, the voice of a small child.

My father leaned over and took her hand, she gave her head a little shake, and said, in her normal voice, "How silly of me! For a moment I was reliving silly childhood fears."

Then she turned to me, "Did you put your hairbrush back into the suitcase? You didn't leave it on the dressing table of the hotel, did you?"

We had one day in Cape Town before the ship left, so we went up the cable car to the top of Table Mountain. From a distance Table Mountain is picture-postcard pretty, but close up it is rugged and craggy and beautiful. From the top one can see the turbulence of the meeting of two great oceans, the Indian and the Atlantic at the end of a mountainous peninsula. I asked, but we never went up Devil's Peak to see the sculpture called *Physical Energy* by Watts at Rhodes Memorial.

We only saw the awesome Devil's Peak from below as we drove past, merely drove past, my mother's old school, because my father wanted to see where she had spent so many years of her life. On the way there she reminisced lightheartedly about boarding school pranks, and about the hockey team and the eccentric teachers, but when we drove past the school she became still and staring. Once again I felt the tiniest inkling of understanding the terror on the train. How terrifying for a highly strung, highly sensitive little farm girl, bearing the Dutch name of a father she never knew, to have to face up alone to the grandeur and snobbishness of this very English school.

Only very recently have I also come to realise that the happy, comfortable Gran I knew, must have been very different from the Gran my mother knew as a little girl. My mother was only two when her father died, and Gran, only a young girl herself at the time, would have been grief-stricken at the sudden and shocking loss of her beloved young husband, and all his family. Not only would she have been grief-stricken, but on that vast and very isolated farm, which she had inherited from her in-laws, she would have felt isolated, frightened, lonely and very insecure. Perhaps my mother still carries the pain and insecurity of those early years deep inside her.

Yet she was a different person on the ship, she loves ships. She loved dressing up for dinner, she partied and danced and laughed and chatted and even played the piano at an impromptu concert. She seemed to shed, like a false skin, her fears on the train, but I took on the burden of her nightmare. Even now I sometimes dream of being on a train hurtling me at great speed in the wrong direction, to the wrong destination, the wrong destiny.

Back home Mother and Father both seemed restless, and talked constantly about going to Canada or Australia, but then my mother became pregnant, and three and a half years ago, my baby brother was born. He is the apple of my parents' eyes; they are quite besotted with him. No wonder! He is the first baby my father has seen grow up, and he is such a GOOD baby. When he was a year old he would sleep all night, and have two day naps, eat anything that was put in his mouth, and sit for hours, smiling happily in his pram or playpen. My mother said I was a dreadful baby at that age; I would not sleep, nor eat, nor ever sit still for one second, but was always running off and disappearing. The only time they could keep track of me was when I was firmly strapped in a red blanket on Dinah's back. She reminded me that Ethel and Iris were the only ones who had the energy to keep track of me, and the only ones who could steer me back from my wayward explorations.

No wonder my placid little brother is such a delight to Mother; no wonder both my parents love him so much.

Of course I went to a different school this time, a girls' preparatory school; and this time I had the good sense not to make it a re-run of my previous school experience.

Gone was the brashness, the feisty fighting spirit that made me stand up and argue for what I felt to be true, on my very first morning at my first school.

Then, I had been self-willed and different; but to be honest, I had to admit that I had always been self-willed and different, it just had not seemed a problem in my life in Africa. There, my friends and I could not have been more different! I was a different colour, I often spoke a different language, I had different interests and aspirations, like reading, and painting and finding things out.

I wore different clothes, my companions could go near-naked in summer, but I was supposed to cover my fair skin from the harsh high-altitude sun, something I fought against at first, but eventually accepted.

Yes we were different alright, but we rather enjoyed our differences, we would laugh and giggle at our differences.

Usually I was the different one, but not always. Just before I left, Iris and I were still little girls, flat as pancakes, but Ethel had begun to grow little breast buds. Iris and I giggled uproariously at this new phenomenon, but Ethel seemed quite proud of the little bumps on her chest!

Yet some differences seemed quite illogical!

For instance I could not work out a logical reason for the fact that once a native woman was married, she began to wear a turban to hide her hair, and long red skirts, to cover her legs, yet she and all the other women were still quite happy to go about barebreasted. The women in my family on the farm were the opposite, they exposed their hair, and, in short dresses on the tennis court, their legs, but never, in public, their breasts.

My mother and her sisters seemed pleased to have thin hips and the tiniest behinds, and what they had, they squashed and flattened with things they called step-ins. The women in the mountains on the other hand, were enormously endowed, and they were proud as peacocks of their huge derrieres; they arched their backs and pushed their buttocks back to emphasise them. The most beautiful could balance a small gourd on their buttocks. Sometimes they would look at me, shake their heads, and click their tongues, saying to me in their language, their tongues going clickety-click in their genuine concern, "If you do not soon begin to grow a tail, you will never find a husband!"

They made me very aware of my dismal lack, because, like them, I saw nothing but beauty in their rounded, naked derrieres. Nudity did not bother me in the slightest, nor did the little boys' "teemies" wobbling as they ran. Now that I think of it, everyone else on the farm, even the two old aunts and my mother and my father were quite unperturbed by nudity, and these days my parents, so conservative in many other ways, still go about the house without clothes when it is warm enough.

But of course I never mention anything like this at school, where the culture is SO different, where one dare not be different.

When I first arrived I was painfully aware of how different I was, and the only way to hide my eccentricities was to be a silent, unobtrusive observer. It was not a passive silence, however; I was actively listening, noting, analysing. So when, at last, I spoke, I sounded exactly like the other children; the same accent, the same inflections, the same phraseology, the same slang and colloquial words, and no big words.

The words of the little boy at my last school still stung, "You are a show-off! You use stupid big words to show off."

I had also been watching and observing the teachers, so there were no requests to explore different avenues. I soon worked out that one did one's work exactly as the teacher wanted it, down to the finest detail. Never mind if I had a quicker or more efficient, or more exciting, or more creative way to tackle the task, I suppressed all such urges, and did it all their way. I never questioned them or challenged them, because I had learned only too well the inherent risks of speaking one's mind. If some of the time I was bored out of my mind, I did not let it show; no more observable yawning.

At first it was torture, and sometimes I had to fight unshed tears of frustration, but fortunately, humans are creatures of habit, and if you force yourself to dumb down your thinking, and speech, and words, after a while habit takes over. In fact after a while I knew that I was no longer only acting just dumb enough to fit in, I was really and truly becoming dumber and dumber and dumber.

My first teacher was quite the opposite of old, icy, Miss Ashburn. Miss Shepherd was young and warm, and exuded an aura of caring, full of gushing praise, and gold stars, for the least little thing. For the first few weeks I longed to bask in the warmth of that caring, sharing aura, I yearned to do something extra special to elicit an especially enthusiastic expression of approval.

One day Miss Shepherd told us to write a poem for homework, a poem about anything at all. I had never written a poem before, though I had often played around with words, making collections of words and phrases that pleased me. Little groups of words that repeated shapes and patterns of meaning the way a painter will repeat patterns of colour, or a sculptor makes rhythms of shapes, or a composer repeats notes.

I had been a silent reader for so long that I still saw script as signs and symbols and shapes, rather than sound; and the shape of a word was influenced by its first letter and its meaning.

I went on thinking about words at my desk at home, for a long time, as I stared out at the overcast sky through the tracery of bare pear tree twigs. For a while I found myself doodling down those delicate tracery patterns, and weaving my favourite words into the drawing. Then winding itself among my words, came wafting and wandering an idea so fragile and flimsy that it frequently faded and fragmented, an idea surely too gigantic, too grand to grasp.

Then the idea and the words began to dance together, until they formed themselves into a poem. The shape of the words gave form to the idea; the form of the poem gave shape to the words.

Trembling with excitement, filled with wonderment and delicious delight, with a kind of exultation that made my whole being quiver with inspiration, I scribbled into my exercise book. I scribbled and scribbled and crossed out and rewrote, until my mother came in to tell me it was very late, time to put the light out, to go to bed. All night words danced in my dreams, and every now and then I would wake up, turn on my torch, and rub out and write down.

The last time I woke, the grey light of dawn was all I needed to see my page; a page crinkled and creased from all that rubbing out and rewriting, so I ran down to the study, and took from the desk a sheet of heavy parchment paper, and the pen that Mother used to handwrite her dinner invitations. My mother does things so nicely, her invitations are always beautifully written on parchment, carefully blotted with her curved amber blotter, and then the envelopes sealed with a round red blob of sealing wax into which she presses the amber seal with her initials beautifully engraved into the amber, so that they stand out in high relief from the wax seal.

Back in my room I copied out the poem, gave it a name, "The Soul of the Universe" and beautifully, like a sculptured pattern, arranged the words in different length lines, some four or five words, sometimes only one magnificent word in a line by itself. Because the idea was so nebulous, the first two lines were flimsy delicate f-words, then I enticed the idea with a duet of lines alternating soft, sensuous, sensual s-words with warm wonderful w-words. By the end, the words and idea were so beautiful in themselves that they no longer needed alliteration to give them shape.

It was so beautiful that I thought I would burst with joy.

At breakfast Mother said, "You are very chirpy today!"

Driving me to school, my father said, "You are sparkling like a sparkler on Guy Fawkes night! Is something special happening at school today?"

I desperately wanted to show him my poem right then and there, but had already decided it would be even better later, with Miss Shepherd's gold star and words of praise on top.

As I handed her the stiff sheet of parchment I heard drumrolls and a trumpeting fanfare in my mind, I did a little invisible curtsey, and had to consciously stop myself from smiling from ear to ear, because I felt that I was solemnly and ceremoniously proffering precious pearls of wisdom. I had rolled the parchment like a scroll, and had been tempted to seal it with my mother's sealing wax, except that I could not really use her monogram on my work.

Mine was the lowest mark in the class for that poem. Five out of ten.

"FIVE!" exclaimed Linda who sat next to me. "Don't tell me you ONLY got five!" She put her hand to her mouth as though it was the most terrible thing, as though it were a nought; but then Miss Shepherd was far too kind and caring to give anything less than five, so it was as bad as a nought. Mine was the only five, most of the class scored eights and nines, and there were even three ten out of tens. Linda was one of those tens, and with the other two girls had to stand out in the front of the class and read her poem.

I did not hear a single word they read, I was too busy tearing my beautiful, thick parchment into shreds, tearing, ripping, shredding it into little tiny pieces like confetti. Nobody noticed, all eyes were on the three girls reading out the front.

A month later we were given another poem for homework. I knew I was far, far too stupid to write a poem, so the next day I was sick, I told my mother that I had a tummy ache and chest pains and a headache, so she let me stay at home.

I was sick again, a month later, the next time a poem was due, but the day I went back to school three girls read out their poems to the class, and as I had nothing else in my mind for the moment I listened to them, and tried to work out the formula for a good poem. When we next had to write a poem for homework I used the formula: it told a story, it was in two square blocks of four lines each, and most important, the ends of the words sounded the same, like simple nursery rhymes. It was not the shape of the word nor the beginning of the word, not alliteration nor assonance, but the sound of its ending that mattered, not the look, only the sound.

It was an awfully ordinary little poem, and as I went to hand it to Miss Shepherd I folded over the paper, and then folded it again and again, until it was only a little square hiding the words that shamed me.

That poem got ten out of ten. I had to stand up and read it out in front of the class. For a wild and wonderful moment I felt an almost irresistible urge to yell out at the top of my voice, "This is such a plain and silly poem!" the way I had told Miss Brown that her reader was a plain and silly book, I wanted to say "I know a much better poem," the way I had offered to tell a better story than Miss Ashburn's ordinary, everyday story; but of course I did not, I suppressed all such urges, and submitted myself instead to Miss Shepherd's effusive praise. Besides, I could not remember my first poem.

I had shredded it in my memory as surely as I had shredded it on parchment.

Miss Shepherd's praise, which I had longed for so desperately, striven for so hard, which was now so effusively heaped upon my head, seemed strangely meaningless and empty.

Miss Shepherd, I had discovered, might be kind and caring, and always terribly nice to everyone, but she knew very little, not a fraction of the things about nature and science that my father told me, not a miniscule atom of what Gran knew, and although she often came out with proverbs and wise sayings, they did not sound anywhere near as wise to me as the sayings of the wise Old Grandfather of the mountains. One day I heard her tell one of the parents rather proudly that she had done a course in "pastoral care," and instantly a picture flashed across my mind of a shepherd minding a flock of thirty sheep; but the picture gallery of my mind rejected that image, and what hangs there instead is an image of a kind and caring, warm and woolly ewe, with a flock of gambolling lambs around her.

But my mother thought Miss Shepherd was wonderful, such a clever teacher, to have tamed my waywardness with her kindheartedness. She told everyone what an excellent teacher I had.

I have to admit that Miss Shepherd taught me one valuable lesson: to reduce everything to a formula. The formula might change from time to time; for instance my present English teacher does not expect poems to rhyme, she likes blank verse, and descriptions, not stories. The formula now is adjectives. Fling in as many as possible, even if they do not make much sense, in fact especially if they do not make much sense, as long as there are plenty of deep and seemingly meaningful emotive adjectives!

I learned to work to a formula and to curb all my own wild and wonderful ideas. If anything I wrote, or painted, made me tremble and quiver with delight, made me sparkle like a sparkler on Guy Fawkes night, then I knew immediately that it was dangerous, that it must be destroyed at once. I produced only safe work, hoping only to fit in unobtrusively, to conform, yet to my amazement, the teachers started sending home reports saying that I was quite brilliant, even though I knew only too well that the work I did for them was so, so ordinary.

After a few terms they even reported that I had become socially well-adjusted. It was easy to work out that being "socially well-adjusted" too, could be reduced to a formula, and could also be used as a form of self-defence or camouflage.

One not only spoke like one's peers, one acted like them, dressed like them, behaved like them; raved on about whatever or whoever was the current rage, and denigrated, ever so wittily and ironically, whosoever or whatever was out of fashion.

By the time I moved into the senior school, I was part of a tight-knit group, frivolous, snobby, but redeemed by just a hint of rebellion, a tendency, now and then, to thumb its nose at authority!

One such instance was with our school uniform. For everyday school days we wore a navy blue serge tunic over a white shirt, with long black stockings.

The tunic was meant to be six inches above the knee (though some mothers bought them even longer so that their daughters could "grow into" them.) We thought we looked terribly dowdy in our serge tunics, and tried to make them look better by tying the belt around our waists very tight, then hoisting up the tunic to make it much shorter. Our legs looked better, but the great roll of extra serge above the waist looked awful. So one day we all (all the girls in our exclusive little group) decided to cut several inches off the bottom of our tunics. What a difference it made! Our uniform was transformed, in our eyes, from being drearily dowdy, to quite cute. The trouble was that some of us went too far, made our tunics so short that our gaps showed, and not just when we rode our bikes past the boys' school!

Sooner or later the teachers twigged that more that just a growth spurt was going on! Every girl in the school had to kneel down on the floor and have her hemline measured with a ruler. Our mothers had to buy us new uniforms.

By the way, if you do not know what a "gap" is, it is the gap of bare fleshed upper leg, between regulation navy bloomers and the scalloped top of black stockings held up by three suspenders, two in front and one at the back!

So, gradually, I began to fit in, on the surface, if not always deep down, by acting the part.

I acted so well that soon I was given the leading role in the school play. Of course, I realised that the teachers had not for a moment realised that I was acting; that they had chosen me merely because I was good at memorising lines.

Being good at games was another part of the formula. It meant that one was one of the first picked when teams were chosen, and then everybody thought how popular one was.

Father was pleased at the suggestion that I was good at games and arranged for me to have tennis coaching. He and his older brother Patrick were almost obsessively competitive, and because Patrick had won a Wimbledon doubles title while studying medicine at Guy's Hospital, my father had been determined to do the same, only to be thwarted, in his opinion, by the war. Perhaps he thought I would fulfil his unfulfilled ambition, though I knew, miserably, from the very first lesson, that I could never live up to such expectations.

Recently, Father has taken notice of me, has been pleased with me once more, because I am doing well in Physics and Chemistry. Now, while his attitudes on some subjects are old-fashioned, as far as women are concerned (perhaps influenced by his remarkably liberated Victorian grandmother), he believes that there is no reason why women cannot, and should not, excel in the sciences; after all his own sister did; and furthermore, he sees no reason why girls should not study medicine and become successful surgeons. He seems to think that it is quite natural to assume that because I am good at science, and show an interest in his work, and because I often draw from his anatomy books, that I want to become a surgeon.

His assumption, perhaps assertion, seems to have filtered through to my teachers, and has become the accepted prognosis for my future.

The Headmistress is pleased. "So nice to see our young ladies challenge the male-dominated professions," she said jovially, the other day, "and with those deft hands of yours you will be a fine surgeon, able to cut and snip, and sew the patients together again with tiny, neat stitches."

I was not sure whether she was joking, or whether that was really her view of surgery.

As I walked out of her office I felt suffocated and trapped. Then I pulled myself together. I conceded to myself, dully, that to please Father and to please the Headmistress I would settle for being a doctor. In many ways it seemed a fine and altruistic thing to do. When I thought logically, the way they wanted me to think, the idea of being a sculptor seemed wayward, and selfish, and strangely perverse; as remote from present realities as my life in the mountains.

When I thought logically, the way I was beginning to think most of the time, it seemed so much wiser to stick to things that were easy, where I did not have to face the embarrassment of failing. It was easy to come first in the year, easy to be in the school play, when the writer did the real inventing; easy to merely study great scientists or great writers or great artists and innovators.

Sculpture, I felt instinctively, meant going out on a limb, it would be full of pitfalls; there were so many elements to juggle, so many problems to solve, so many abstract concepts; so many antitheses, it was at once so nebulous and yet so concrete and enduring. There were so many passing fads and fashions. The risks of failure, or worse, of settling for a formula, conforming to trends, which would mean settling for mediocrity, were enormous.

That is what both my logical mind and my very tender and vulnerable ego told me; so that together they subdued the little inner cry that pleaded and yearned for a challenge, for something really difficult.

Besides, there seems to be not the faintest opportunity to do any sculpture, although we did have "art" while I was still at prep school. Art was painting, on Friday afternoons not with an art teacher, but our class teacher. In my last year at the prep we had a terribly strict teacher, and a great believer in rote learning; so we could recite all the kings and queens of England, the capital cities of all the countries in Europe, the parts of a flower, maths theorems, the books of the Bible, school rules, and several rousing, didactic poems. Her one concession to student-initiated activity was Friday afternoon art. By that time she was so exhausted from all that strictness that she would merely say, after lunch, "Get out your art things and work quietly please," before retiring, worn out, wrung out, limp as a rag, to doze behind the piles of our exercise books on her desk.

That year I had been given for my birthday another watercolour paint box and a few sheets of handmade paper, made from cloth, not wood. One day, as I was running my fingertips over the rough texture of the paper, wondering what I should paint, I had a flashing recollection of the image of Landi's hand caressing the rusticated stone of the stable walls, and knew that I must paint those walls onto this paper. Not the exterior, bleached in the brilliant African light but the interior, cool and dark.

I drew the blocks lightly in pencil, and then laid on my watercolours; purple and prussian and umbers, raw umber and burnt umber. They blended and ran and marbled and crackled, forming misty mauves and shadowy sepias. I kept layering and texturing all afternoon, then added, towards the end a rough wooden manger, and straw on the floor, and the old horse who used to sneak back into the cool dark stables, out of the searing heat, and hide in the shadows, thoughtfully munching all day long.

Just before the bell went, the teacher walked around to see what we had done.

"That is a very dark painting," she said to me.

"Yes," I said.

The next week I added my mother cat, down in the bottom corner, sitting smiling complacently at her seven kittens tumbling, tussling, stalking, pouncing, leaping, somersaulting, cuffing. Then I went back to my wonderful wall, adding yet more layers, more texturing.

The painting became a doorway for my imagination; looking into it was like walking through that real stable doorway, from the searing heat and blinding light outside, feeling the coolness caress one's bare, sunburnt arms. I could smell the manure and straw and sweet government sugar, dampened in its bag by a storm, stored in the stable for the horses. I felt laughter bubbling up as I saw the kittens' antics.

When the teacher came around this time she said, "The cats are good, but why is the painting so dark?"

"Because there were no windows in the stables," I replied.

She did not have anything more to say, but I was a little indignant that she kept harping on the darkness, as did my friends, echoing her, when they came over to look at what I had done after the bell had gone.

After all I had seen a book in the library on Rembrandt, and all his paintings were dark. To confirm my conviction, on Saturday I went back to the library, found the book, and found that I had been wrong. Rembrandt's paintings were not all dark, as I remembered them. They were mostly dark, but often there were touches of brilliant lights and golds, seemingly in thick pasty paint, though it was hard to tell in reproduction.

There was not a white palette in my watercolour box, so I asked my mother to buy me a tube of white paint so that I could try to imitate Rembrandt's highlights. Yet when I squeezed it out onto my palette the next Friday at school, it looked awful, like toothpaste, like the white paste we use to whiten our white shoes, impossible to add to my shadowy painting. Even when I added a little umber and a touch of blue to it, to tone it down, it seemed quite wrong for the mood of my painting. Then suddenly I took up my pen nib, lying next to my inkwell, scooped up the streaky white lump and smeared, dragged, spattered a suggestion of the flapping wings of the white hen who had fluttered and flustered and bustled her brood of chickens down from the nest in the manger so long ago. Following behind her, in naples yellow mixed into the thick whitish sludge, three fluffy, fluttering chicks. Then I dragged, with a dry brush, the dry remains of the white paint over the paws of the kittens, catching only the surface textures of the rough, handmade paper, like fur picking up the light, and with the leftover yellow, just barely touched their tiger stripes. I was so fascinated by the effect that I was tempted to highlight the old horse as well; but I resisted the temptation and left him, as he was, lurking unobtrusively in the shadows. Instead I blobbed in, in pure vermilion, the comb of the hen.

Just then the teacher came around. "That will do as an animal painting! The Head wants us to enter some art in the R.S.P.C.A. competition," and she picked up my painting.

I wanted to cry "No no no!" but that had not prevented them taking my Bushman stone away from me, so I was silent.

A week later the school received a curt letter saying, "We trust the painting titled *Stable* was the unaided work of the child," and I felt my heart sink, because I should have known that a slight sparkly feeling I had while painting that picture would cause trouble.

My teacher was angry and indignant, and I was summoned to the headmistress's office. In the end the strict class teacher sent back an even curter letter saying that she had seen the painting done, "Right under my nose." I only know because I had to sign it too.

A few weeks later I received a gold-embossed certificate and a cheque for five guineas, and the school received a bundle of animal books for the library. They kept my painting. The headmistress was pleased and announced the award in the school magazine. The headline: "School wins National Art Prize" made a nice cultural counter to the usual, "School Wins Hockey Tournament," but the article underneath was mainly about the Royal Society for the Prevention of Cruelty to Animals.

That was the last year the whole class did Art at school. In this school hardly anyone takes Art as a subject, only those who really and truly cannot cope with Latin are allowed to, so it is considered a subject for dummies.

Yet on the strength of that win, once or twice teachers asked me to do a painting for a competition, and to my surprise, sometimes I won a prize. The last competition I entered, the last competition I vow I will ever, ever enter, was earlier this year. For the first time it was held nearby.

Another girl from my school, who does art, Hazel Stone, won first prize, and I came second. We were escorted and chaperoned by the Deputy to the award-presentation and cocktail party, a smart gathering of men in dinner suits and ladies in cocktail hats. I felt a little surge of pride to see my work hanging there in an annex of the hall near some very good paintings by real, well-known artists.

The school children had been given a title to work to: "The Harvesters", as the Arts Festival was part of the larger Harvest Festival. Hazel had painted figures harvesting wheat, while I had painted some bright green apple trees, swirly, contorted apple trees because I had been so impressed with Van Gogh's olive trees, with bright red apples, being harvested by pickers up a white ladder. One of the boys from the boys' grammar school had been more original, he had drawn a modern mechanical harvester, very detailed and technically correct. He had been awarded a Highly Commended.

I wandered around the room looking at the other entries and then, at the very end of the room, at the opposite end from the winners, I stopped short in front of a small painting. Seen from a low viewpoint, as though the painter was lying on the ground under the figures, three peasant women, wielding three great white sickles, cutting golden hay. The design had a wonderful rhythm, the three curving, bending backs, echoing the curving scythes, repeating the curved lines of the wind-blown wheat. The colours flat, stark and simple, with no shading; grey figures, black shadows, white sickles, yellow ochre hay. Yet the painting also had feeling; the feeling of both hardworking, back-breaking, body-aching labour, and also of grace and harmony.

"This is bloody marvellous!" I muttered to myself. Then I noticed the name underneath, Silvia Hammond. I had never talked to her, but I knew of her, everybody at our school did. She was from India, but not Indian, and because the climate was considered unhealthy for English schoolchildren she had to come back to boarding school. She hated it, and twice had tried to escape. The first time she had been found at the local railway station, but the next time she was more wily, and had been missing for two days. The school was frantic, until she was found, far away, at the dockyards, trying to stow away on a ship to India. I guessed that she loved India as ferociously as I loved Africa.

Just then there was an announcement in the main hall, and the deputy head put her hand on my shoulder to escort me in to the presentation ceremony. As the mayor gave his speech I was making up a speech of my own. I would say, "I am sorry your honour, I cannot accept a prize, when there is a painting in there that is much, much better than mine, than any of the winners, and it was not even commended."

When Hazel Stone received her prize she curtseyed beautifully, smiled charmingly at the Mayor, and beamed around at the clapping crowd. I followed, frowning furiously, furious at my own cowardice, at not having the courage to utter my little speech, furious at the judges. I did not curtsey, nor smile, and barely mumbled a thank you.

My churlishness delighted Hazel Stowe.

"What's the matter, Smarty Pants? Cheesed-off because you did not win first prize this time?" she taunted me. The deputy head must have made the same interpretation because she frowned at me, pursed her lips and escorted us home immediately.

A few days later I saw Silvia Hammond alone in the playground. She is a year ahead of me, so I had never spoken to her before, but I went up to her and said, "I saw your painting in the competition, it was marvellous. The judges got it all wrong, you should have won!"

For a moment I thought she was going to smile, but the smile turned into a sneer, and she turned away from me. "What makes you think you are a better judge than the judges, Smarty?"

"You see!" I admonished myself later as I retreated to lick my wounds, "When you ignore your formula for being accepted, when you try to say what you really feel, or to express what you really believe, it is always a disaster!"

Mother, whom I desperately wanted to please, was not quite as pleased as I hoped she would be about my academic success, nor my art prizes. I could not quite put my fingers on what it was, but it seemed to make her uneasy, so I began to feel uneasy about it myself. When she introduced me to her friends or to other mothers of girls at my school, they would sometimes gush, "So this is your brainy daughter? You must be very proud of her." Mother would always respond very quickly, saying something along the lines of their daughter being so pretty, so vivacious, having such exquisite manners!

Fortunately for her peace of mind, I was invited to some of the best parties, and she assumed that if I were always going to parties, I must be fitting in, and therefore happy. I could never understand why she equated parties and popularity with happiness.

CHAPTER FOURTEEN

THE WISDOM OF THE ANCIENTS

"Claim nothing. Enjoy."

EESHA UPANISHAD

I remember one of those parties, my friend Carol's, a few months ago. We are at an in-between age for parties now, too old for games and clowns and Punch and Judy shows, yet not quite old enough for dances and dinner parties. Not yet boy mad; in fact in my group we still proclaim vehemently that boys are boring and stupid though I have a sneaking feeling that that is all about to change. So this was an all girls' afternoon tea party, a table groaning with a mouthwatering array of prettily presented food, enjoyed with lots of giggling and gossip. I was the last guest left, after everyone else had said their thank-yous and goodbyes, because my mother had told Carol's mother that she would be a little late.

Cacs (we call her that) and I went back to the dining room to have another go at the leftovers.

"You know how alcoholics are addicted to alcohol, well I am addicted to chocolate," she mumbled, tucking into a plate of hand-made chocolates from the new shop in town. "Does that make me a chocoholic!" Carol's mother had certainly catered for her daughter's taste, as well as bowls of chocolates there were chocolate biscuits, chocolate eclairs and the birthday cake with candles had also been a rich, dark chocolate. Fortunately for me there were also some sand-wiches and fruit cake left over. I am not mad about chocolate, but I love fruit cake.

"You're a fruit cake, a nut-case for not liking chocolate," laughed Cacs. We were both silently munching when her brother walked in.

"Did the ravenous hordes leave anything for me?" he said to his sister as he came into the room, then he saw me.

"Oh, I see one of them is still here, and still stuffing herself." As he spoke he picked up a plate and loaded it with an incongruous mix-ture of sweet and savoury, of sausage rolls, sandwiches, meringues and eclairs.

Carol's brother is a few years older than we are, at university, study-ing political history and social science and very full of himself. I had met him briefly once or twice before, but we had never exchanged more than a few platitudes. Now he said, between mouthfuls,

"You're the one from Africa, aren't you?" I still had my mouth full too, so I merely nodded.

"Well you might just be of use to me. You see I am writing a thesis, projecting future major political issues. Now I firmly believe that racial prejudice will be the big, big issue in the coming decades. Tell me, did you find much in Africa?"

"Well," I said, "not really. But I had the impression that feelings were not always the best between the English and the Dutch." I was far too embarrassed to mention that my mother had a Dutch father, and that some of my father's sisters-in-law held that against her.

"No, stupid child. I meant blacks and whites."

"You mean brown and pink? Natives and Europeans?" I countered, stung by being called stupid, and by the realisation that I had not understood what he meant, that I was a little bit hazy about the word prejudice, which I thought simply meant pre-judging someone or some issue, and which I had really only encountered before in *Pride and Prejudice*.

"No," I went on, "I didn't notice any."

"Nonsense!" he said, "I don't believe you. You said before that you lived on a farm; now you can't tell me that the blacks, the native workers I mean, were treated exactly the same as the whites?"

"Well," I smiled, "the only white workers we had apart from the family were locked up at night. They were Italian prisoners of war. The natives were free. So you see, on our farm the natives were free, but the Europeans were prisoners!"

"Be serious," he groaned.

"Well seriously," I said, finding myself actually relishing a serious argument. "Two things. When I was there I really felt in my bones that there was more tension between some of the English and the some Dutch or Afrikaaners, than there was between the Europeans and the natives. Some people of Dutch descent still had vivid and unforgiving memories of their mothers and sisters dying in concentration camps in the Boer war, while many English still had a snooty superior attitude towards the Dutch. Just as here in England, now in the fifties, nine years after the war, there is sometimes more antipathy towards Germans among some people than towards Jamaicans.

"Secondly, yes, we had more material things than the natives, but the difference between us and the natives was a lot less than the difference between some landowners who live in palatial stately homes here in England and their tenant farmers or lowly workers who live in unheated little hovels, even though they are exactly the same race. So there!"

"You're trying to equate the race war with the class discrimination. Well let me tell you, I think the class war is in the past, the race war will be the future. This month there has been a supreme court case in America about segregated schools. The first rumblings, in my opinion, of something that is going to be a shift in thinking.

"In Australia the Aborigines can't vote, or even go into pubs, but there are some signs of change even there. In twenty or thirty years from now, race and colonialism will be a major issue. And the big war, the real guns and bombs war will be in South Africa. That is what I am forecasting in my thesis! Already, right now there is war in Kenya against the Mau Mau. But that won't last; there are too few whites, most of them have only been there a short while, and they will just pack up and come back to England. But the Afrikaaners have nowhere to go home to. The very name they have given themselves suggests that they think of themselves as Africans, their ancestors have been there for three hundred years, so they will fight to the bitter end for what they think is their country. And they will be motivated by the strongest motivator of all, and that is fear.

"Remember, we now live in the Atomic Age. Since the bombs were dropped on Japan, everyone is making atom bombs. We are busy testing atom bombs in the deserts of Australia, the Americans are making hundreds more, and testing hydrogen bombs on Bikini Atoll in the Pacific, the Russians are making hydrogen bombs, soon the Chinese and everybody else will make nuclear weapons; atom bombs, hydrogen bombs, and who knows what else! So will the South Africans; they are clever, and with all those gold and diamond mines, wealthy enough to produce atom bombs, so, even if it takes twenty years or so, there is going to be one hell of a civil war."

"How ridiculous!" I cried, appalled at the way this young man seemed to almost relish the idea of atomic warfare, appalled at the thought of my friends caught up in a war.

"You can't use The Bomb in a civil war, you would blow yourself up too."

"Ah, but they're being cunning. There is talk of separating the races, having different homelands. THEN you could have an atomic war. And the blacks will have atomic bombs or hydrogen bombs too; the Chinese and Russians will supply them!"

"Look," I could not bear to contemplate his scenario, "by that time, in twenty or thirty years I mean, the natives will probably have the vote, and there won't be any need for your war."

"What an unbelievably stupid ignoramus you are! Do you realise what you are saying? It is all very well for the Americans to give the Red Indians the vote, because they wiped out most of them; and no doubt one of these days the Australians will give the Aborigines the right to vote because there are so few of them. But in Africa the whites are a small minority, and they are frightened. And fear is the strongest motivator of all. They are terrified of anarchy and chaos, scared stiff at how tenuous their hold over their own destiny. Because if the native majority had the vote in South Africa they would win government, and all the whites would have to hand over control of the police, the army, schools, hospitals, everything!

"Look, how could the Afrikaaners even contemplate giving over control to the blacks when they themselves would have to go on living there, as a fear-filled minority because there is nowhere else for them to go!"

"Well, I think they might just!" I refused to give in.

"What an idiotic idea! Why on earth would they do that?"

"Well maybe not in one fell swoop. Gradually, progressively. That's it. Progressively. Like at first giving the chiefs and elders of each tribe a seat in parliament. Then giving the vote to natives with a degree. Then the next election everybody with a certain level of schooling, or a business of their own. Sort of give the message that study and hard work are better ways of having a say in the running of your country than running around with guns shooting white farmers like the Mau Mau in Kenya."

"What nonsense! That will never happen."

"Well I still believe it just might! Because in that country I always sensed a feeling of consideration and of … of … reasonableness. Yes that is it, reasonableness!" I suddenly thought of telling him the story of John and the corpse, and Gran's definition of reasonableness, but just then my mother walked in with Carol's mother.

Well, I thought, at least I had the last word: "reasonableness!"

I was still shaken and angry, but remembered my manners enough to hide my fury behind a gushing veneer of the rituals of thank you for a lovely party, and all that.

In the car going home I burst out "I am never going there again! Carol's brother called me stupid and idiotic and an ignoramus."

"I wouldn't let it worry you," said my mother absentmindedly.

This made me feel even more indignant. That is exactly what she had said about Miss Ashburn and the little boys who tormented me at my first school, and I never got used to it, never stopped worrying about it. For a while I sat there silently seething with indignation.

Then suddenly, I saw myself in a detached sort of a way; I stood outside the "me" all immersed in indignation and self-righteousness like a five year old. Mother is absolutely right, I suddenly thought in amazement, why should I let it worry me. If I really think about it, I actually enjoyed the verbal joust with Carol's brother, as much as all the giggling and gossip with my friends. And it made me think about things. The atom bomb for instance. Well not that really, we all think about the bomb all the time; even my seemingly flippant friends are always bringing it into the conversation; it seems to hang over us like the Sword of Damocles.

But he made me think about things like prejudice, and different races, and how the world was changing, and would go on changing. How my thinking kept changing and would go on changing. Back when I lived in Africa, I thought that Africa was a land of plenty and that poverty was something that was found in Europe, among the refugees, after the war; that England was the place of food shortages. I remember when my Uncle Patrick (the one who won Wimbledon while he was a medical student at Guy's Hospital) and his wife, Joy and my cousin Mickey visited us in Africa, passing through to investigate a hospital posting in Durban.

Mickey's eyes had lit up at the breakfast table with the tray of eggs, bacon and chops. "Ooo," he had exclaimed. "Can I really and truly have two eggs?"

Yet soon after breakfast he had been violently sick all over the place.

"He has never in his life eaten anything as rich as two eggs at the same meal," explained his mother.

Until then I had never thought of eggs as rich and precious. Even my brown friends would not consider eggs anything special.

Yet, more than his comments about poverty and prejudice, I worried about Cac's brother's predictions about war. What if he was right about an atomic civil war in my beloved Africa? No, I thought, I refuse to believe it. I really should have told him that story. Only a little anecdote, just another little piece in the overall picture that, together with so much else, convinced me in my heart that there might just be enough compassion and reasonableness in the consciousness of enough people, to avert his terrible predictions.

I remember it so well.

On our farm there were two Bushmen, an elderly man and his wife who were not really "our natives" but newcomers. About two years earlier they had arrived and said to my grandfather that the farm they had been living on had been sold, and that they were now coming to live in our kraal. My step-grandfather said that he did not really have work, but the man said he did not want to work only to live there. He was a hunter, he would live as his people had always lived, by trapping hares and rabbits and dassies. My grandfather said as long as they did not touch his herd of springbuck!

So they moved in. With the help of the other natives they build a hut above the others, though they seemed to prefer to sleep under the stars on the mountainside in the summer. They were like shadows, ghosts, rarely seen, because they often went "walkabout", hunting and gathering food in the traditional nomadic Bushman way for weeks at a time; and even when they were home, they kept to themselves, and let the others fetch their ration of mealie-meal each month, so that we hardly knew them.

Two days before Christmas one year, Dinah said to Gran that the old lady was very sick. Dinah's old aunt, who played the role of witchdoctor or medicine woman on the farm, had been treating her, but had pronounced dramatically that the old woman was too sick, she was going to die. Could she have some of Gran's white pills to ease her pain and fever?

Gran's medicine chest was the second line of medical defence, and the witchdoctor lady often referred to it. The white pills were aspirin for pain and fever, which some natives thought were quite magical, then there was dettol or gentian violet for wounds and cuts and infected sores (they had much more faith in the bright purple gentian violet) a thick black syrupy mixture for coughs, and a gluggy white mixture for tummy upsets. Not much but it seemed to have coped with most things up until then. Gran gave Dinah the white pills, but also went up to see the old woman, and came back a short while later saying that the symptoms sounded to her very much like appendicitis, and perhaps John, who was going in to collect supplies that day, should take the woman in to see old Doctor Johnstone.

Dr Johnstone agreed that it was acute appendicitis, and sent John straight to the nearest town which had a cottage hospital, another hundred miles away. There things were frantic. There were usually two surgeons, but over the Christmas break one was away, and the other was inundated with local emergencies, and on top of all that a head-on car accident had just added five seriously injured patients to his load. Nonetheless the matron admitted the Bushman woman, putting an armband around her wrist labelling her "Gran's maid" because she could not spell the clicking name. John, meanwhile had a rough journey home, because the radiator in the lorry split, and leaked long before he even reached our own little outpost village. He had to leave the lorry there, and as the car could not hold all the bags of supplies, my grandfather had to pick him up in the ancient old van that was kept on the farm, and very occasionally used to transport lambs, or to take salt-licks across country to the far paddocks for the sheep. It wheezed and rattled and practically ground to a halt on the steeper uphill slopes to the farm. We always joked that its top speed uphill was two miles an hour.

That evening Gran had a phone call from the cottage hospital saying that one of the car accident patients had serious head injuries and had been sent by ambulance to the coast, to a specialist brain surgeon in East London. They had sent "Gran's maid" down in the cab of the ambulance, next to the driver, because she would get into surgery sooner in the big hospital.

The next day was Christmas so we heard nothing. Then on Boxing Day Gran phoned the big hospital. Making a phone call in Africa at that time was no simple matter! First of all we were on a party line, and with everybody wanting to wish all their friends the compliments of the season, and making party arrangements, getting onto the line was hard enough. Then the local exchange lady had to get onto the city exchange lady, and she had to get on to the hospital, and they had to find the patient in the native ward, and then find the matron for that section. Gran seemed to spend all day on the phone, but when at last she spoke to the matron the news was good. Our "maid" had been operated on immediately; her appendix had been very inflamed, but had not burst, she was still heavily sedated because she was so agitated, but all her vital signs like her temperature and pulse and heartrate seemed to be returning to normal.

"She is making an excellent recovery. You can pick her up in ten days' time; early in the New Year," concluded the matron. It was arranged that John would fetch her in the car this time, which would make it a more comfortable journey. He would leave on the second of January, have a day on the town, a swim in the sea, and bring the Bushman's wife home the following day. Except that on New Year's Eve, early in the morning, there was a phone call from the big hospital: the woman had died. Unless the body was claimed immediately it would be buried in the native cemetery. Once more Gran insisted on speaking to the sister in charge of the ward.

"Believe me, physically she was doing just fine," said the sister, "I think she just died of fright. Everything here terrified her! The doctors with their stethoscopes frightened her, the nurses with their syringes terrified her, even the coloured maid with the vacuum cleaner made her cower in terror; and most of all the electric light alarmed her. She was in a constant state of fear, and I think it was all too much for her to bear."

Because it was a party line and several women heard the sister's theory, these women all had stories to tell, some about witchdoctor prophesies making the subsequent death of the subject inevitable, while others told how Bushmen had died simply from being locked up within four walls.

Whatever the cause, Gran had the task of telling the woman's husband, summonsing him to the kitchen door, using Dinah to interpret when she could not understand some of his clickety words.

When she told him that his wife had died he took it quietly, philosophically; it was as he expected, he said, it was predicted by the witchdoctor. But when she said that she would be buried in the native cemetery he became very agitated. If she did not die in the mountains, he said, at least her body must come back, so that her spirit could wander there. He would set out immediately to fetch the body. Gran explained gently that that was impossible, it was many weeks walk away.

"Then," he said, "the little-*baas* must fetch her in that," he pointed to the old van parked outside the wool shed. He did not use the word for "that thing", or for "that creature"; cars were to him I think somewhere in between things and creatures. He could not even call it something like a horseless carriage; in his culture there were neither horses nor wheels.

"Do I have to?" John was aghast. "The lorry is still at the garage being repaired, a coffin would not fit in the car, and that old rattletrap will never make it. Besides, I can't miss tonight's party."

"It is the only reasonable thing to do," was Gran's adamant reply, so he went. In the ancient, rattletrap van.

The New Year's Eve Ball was the social occasion of the year. It was held in the richest farmer's wool shed, but over the years almost everyone became involved; a committee of ladies designed and decorated the wool shed, transforming it into a glittering ballroom, another group organised the dance music, a combination of amateur musicians, a pianist, an accordionist, and two violin players, and when they took a break, gramophone records, on a wind-up gramophone. John was a good dancer, in fact he was always teased and nicknamed "Fred Astaire" for the night, but he loved it, he became the life and soul of the party, and even showed off a bit! I think he especially wanted to show off that year, because the rich farmer's daughter had just arrived home from a long stay with relatives, and he had for a long time had a crush on her.

Of course everybody wanted to know where he was when we arrived without him. An Afrikaans farmer summed up their sympathy.

"Poor bloomin' bugger! Crikey man! It will be 104 in the shade tomorrow, and he'll be cooped up in that old rattletrap all day with a stinking corpse!"

"Well," said Gran tartly, "what else could he do? It was the only reasonable thing to do. If it had been one of your natives you would have done the same thing."

"I s'pose," mused the Afrikaaner. "Ja! I s'pose I would of."

"Every one of you would have gone!" she said, a touch defiantly to the whole group. I had the feeling that although she had given her own son no alternative, she was feeling a little guilty and upset about his missing the party.

"It was the reasonable thing to do!"

"Ja," they all agreed, it was the only reasonable thing to do. Put in the same position they would all have gone to fetch the body.

The next day was, as the Afrikaaner had predicted, 104 blistering degrees in the shade, if one could find any shade. It was not until late in the afternoon, when the sun was burning down towards the western mountain ridge that we at last saw the trail of dust on the distant road, and then a little while later, heard the revving, rattling old van stuttering up the last hillside. By the time it pulled into the gravel yard, the old man was there waiting.

John emerged from the van, and I thought how awful he looked; strained and exhausted, his face white and hollow-cheeked, his khaki clothes crumpled and patchy with dark, wet areas of sweat. Not one bit like his usual debonair, easygoing self.

The old man went up to him and said,

"It is a good thing that you have done. Thank you." Not effusively, no gushing thanks, just quietly, with dignity.

"Thank you," said John, I suppose thanking him for the thanks.

Then, as the old man with the help of Boy and the inside maids went to take the thin plywood coffin from the van, John, almost retching, staggered across the gravel, towards the windmill, the still, silent windmill because there was not a breath of wind that oppressively hot day, and collapsed straight forward, bellyflopping into the cement trough beneath the windmill, even though at that time of the year the lukewarm water was covered with a scum of foamy green algae.

"I wish I could offer him an ice-cold beer, or even iced water," said Gran wistfully, coming to the kitchen door. But she could not; there was no fridge on the farm.

The next day, as usual I awoke just when the first glimmer of dawn was a mere sliver of silver-grey in the gap in the curtains.

I had been dreaming about the dead woman, and about the spirit of the little people, and so, in that first moment of waking, in that half-real state between dreaming and waking, I thought that I heard the spirit of the little people singing in my room. I sat bolt upright and listened, yet when I listened very intently the sound disappeared. Then as soon as I relaxed, there it was again. A high-pitched, ululating, haunting, mournful melody. I shot out of bed. I was already wearing my cotton knickers, so it took me less than a moment to rip off my pyjama top and replace it with a cotton shift. Then I was running down the passage, and out the back door, not bothering about shoes, with time consuming laces, or sandals with awkward buckles, running like a cat on hot bricks across the coarse gravel, and then easily, on the smoothly worn earth, my feet enjoying the contact with the cool, silky-smooth powdery earth, smooth as talcum powder, up the narrow path to the huts. As I ran, the sun struck the topmost peaks of the mountains, and turned the grey-blue granite into molten gold, while down below every-thing was still cool and grey and misty. Even in the hottest weather, the early mornings, before dawn, seemed cool and grey in those mountains. I stopped running, and stood stock still.

"It is so beautiful," I found myself saying out aloud. "Everything is so perfectly beautiful." I stretched my arms above my head, to greet the sun, and to salute the beautiful eagle, because even though I could not see him, I knew he was as that moment soaring toward the new sun.

Then I saw Dinah, and Ethel and Iris, coming down the path towards me just as they had the first day I arrived back on the farm. The sun was rising, yet now its golden light appeared to be moving not up but down the mountain, flowing like golden lava, down over the grey shadows, and then it caught Dinah and her daughters in its thrall, turning them into three light, golden figures, followed by long black shadows, mimicking their every move behind them.

"Listen!" I whispered, when they came close. "What is that sing-ing? Can you hear it?" By now the lovely sounds seemed to be echoing and re-echoing from mountain to mountain to mountain, faint, distant, but movingly beautiful.

"That is a funeral song. The old man and some of the women are going up the mountain to bury the dead woman," said Dinah. So we stood and let our listening go out for a long time.

Then a thought occurred to me, "But it would be impossible. It is all rock up there. How can they bury anyone up there?"

"In his clan they do not dig. Perhaps they will lay the body under some suikerbossie branches. It is near the eyrie of the black mountain vultures, and they will come and take the flesh and bones."

"Oh how awful!"

"No," said Dinah. "That is the custom for the old man's people. He believes that when the birds take some of her bones high, high up in the krantzes to feed their young, then her spirit too will soar high, high in the mountains. And if a jackal comes and takes a bone down into its lair, in the earth, then her spirit will become one with the earth. And if some of the flesh rots, and grasses grow, and the springbok eat the grass, her spirit will run and jump and spring with the springbok. Then the old man will be happy because wherever he goes in the mountains he will know he is surrounded by the spirit of his wife, just as he walks among all the spirits of his ancestors. Last night the old man spoke by the fire. We are all one with the world, and with all the creatures of our world, he said, whether we are alive or dead. It does not make any difference."

Again I stood silently for a long time thinking about what the old Bushman had said. And Dinah and the girls stood silently in the dawn light with me while each of us pondered the unknowable things that one feels and senses but cannot put into words. The singing grew fainter and fainter, until only the echoes remained in the mountains and in our hearts.

At last I felt the need to say something, to break the spell, to return to reality, and so I went back to my last spoken thought.

"But vultures are such ugly birds!"

"The old man would chide you for saying such things," said Dinah. "You are always saying how beautiful the eagle is, how you love to watch the eagle soar. But in the air, from a distance vultures also soar and sweep like the eagles. The old man would say that all creatures are his brothers and sisters, the earth is mother to all, and all play a part in the unity of life."

I sighed, "The thoughts of that old man are very strange to me, but deep down they seem also very beautiful. Is it possible that we are one with all creatures, and that when we die we remain one with everything here on earth? Even the vultures!"

"Is that not what you believe?"

"I think we are meant to believe that we go somewhere else when we die. To a place called Heaven if we are very good, and a terrible fiery furnace called Hell if we are bad."

"That is a very, very strange thing to believe!" exclaimed Dinah. "Now we must hurry, everybody will be wanting their early morning coffee. I also am feeling like my coffee now."

That is the story I thought fleetingly of telling Carol's know-all brother. Not of course my whole rambling recollection of the anecdote, which I am only remembering now, reliving now. If I had told him all this he would really and truly have thought that I was bonkers!

I would have told him only the bare bones of what John had done, and the Afrikaaner's reply, "Ja. I suppose I would have done the same. It was the only reasonable thing to do." I would have told him that to make a point, that all the farmers agreed they would have done the same thing, to point out everybody's attitude of reasonableness; to make him think, realise the real bond there could be between white farmers and their native workers. The way he has made me think. About prejudice. There are all sorts of prejudices, not just white people thinking that they are superior to black people. Men think they are superior to women, humans think they are superior to animals. No one seems to consider the feelings of the dogs and chimps they plan to send up into space, and hunters still shoot tigers and leopards. Then there is religious prejudice. So many wars because of religious prejudice, so many sincere, thinking people tortured and burned at the stake. I wondered whether the discriminators were following their God's example; after all, was not a God who had a "chosen people" discriminating? Then again, perhaps the people just thought they were chosen. I mean, what a weird idea! To imagine God sitting up there and thinking to himself. "Well now, I have created all these different people. Chinese and Indians, and Red Indians, and Siamese. Black people and white people, and my beautiful little Bushmen in Africa. But I will only care about my 'chosen people', a little tribe somewhere in the Middle East." Weird, really, really weird! I really cannot bring myself to believe that.

It was wondering about the ins and outs of religious prejudice that made me almost accidentally choose my History project.

We have a really good history teacher this year, Miss Gardner. Or I think so anyway; a lot of girls in my class make fun of her because she is old and eccentric and waffles on about her pet ideas, and often quotes difficult philosophers and they say they cannot figure out what she is talking about. But I like the way she does not drill us with dates and kings and wars, and concentrates on the history of ideas and art and inventions. We have been studying the Renaissance, and recently she made us do our own research on two Renaissance men (women were not even mentioned as an option!) for homework. She sent us to the school library for a period to choose our subjects, and then went around the class writing down each girl's choice. When it came to my turn I said,

"Donatello and Michelangelo."

"You can't choose two sculptors."

"Well then, Michelangelo the sculptor, and Raphael the painter."

"No, not two artists. And," she added to forestall me, "architects are also artists. What about a statesman, a writer, an explorer, a religious figure, a scientist? You're interested in science, I think you should choose a scientist."

I was tempted to say, "Alright, Leonardo da Vinci, the scientist," but I thought I had already been bold enough, so, still vaguely indignant, and disillusioned and surprised to have found in my recent reading, religious prejudice even in the enlightened Renaissance, I said, "Giordano Bruno."

"Oh." She sounded surprised.

"He was one of the first scientists to suggest that the universe is infinite; he also believed that God is part of everything in creation, and for believing these things the Catholic Church tortured him and had him burned at the stake. In the year 1600, in the flower markets of Rome," I finished with a smile.

"You certainly seem to know a lot about him," she said. "Well then, I'll put you down as Michelangelo and Giordano Bruno."

In fact I knew absolutely nothing about Bruno beyond what I had just glibly recited, because that was all there was about him in the book that I had read. "I'll soon find more," I thought, but I could not. Not in the school library, nor in the books at home. Which was a lovely excuse for getting my mother to take me to the city library.

There I soon found enough for my project, and I was amazed at how modern Bruno's astronomy sounded. He went far beyond Copernicus, suggesting that the universe was infinite and contained many other worlds similar to our solar system. He seemed a very reasonable man, seeking virtue and truth as philosophical investigations. Yet wherever he went, except perhaps in the court of Elizabeth the first in

England, where he was truly admired, he caused controversy and furore. He was excommunicated for suggesting that the individual soul and the universal soul are ultimately one. Then of course he was burned alive. I wondered why it was, that throughout history, reasonable and intellectual figures, from Socrates down, aroused such hatred and fury in the goody-goody people in power. Why is original thinking so dangerous?

I also found several books on Michelangelo.

"It will take me at least two hours to copy out what I need," I said to my mother. "Why don't you go shopping, and go and have a cup of tea at the tearoom."

I had exaggerated the time it would take to make notes, because I love having time to just browse around and read in that vast library.

My friend Carol who is addicted to chocolate was telling me about a dream she had. She dreamt that she walked into the new chocolate shop in our town, the one that not only stocks exotic chocolates from Belgium and Switzerland, but also makes their own chocolates, and licorice, so that you can smell them as you walk in the door. She dreamed that the lady said, "Come in come in, and eat as much as you like, whatever you like." So Carol frantically began eating chocolates. But she could only take a tiny bite out of each one. Soon the whole shop was littered with half-eaten chocolates, silver paper wrappings strewn everywhere, but Carol did not dare finish one, or savour one, or enjoy it, because she was frightened she would be stopped by the lady before she had at least tasted every chocolate in the shop.

I laughed and sympathised with her dream, because that is exactly how I feel when I have a short hour or two in a reference library. I want to try every book, every subject, and end up not having time to read and savour anything at all. Usually I go to the natural history section first, and look for new books on African animals, then I go to the art books.

This time my curiosity had been aroused by the term Neo-Platonism that had recurred over and over both in my reading on Michelangelo and Bruno. The big book in that library on Michelangelo had not only his paintings and sculptures, but also some of his poetry, and I copied some into my project. I could do this because Miss Gardner was the only teacher I knew who would understand, and like it. It matched something she had said in class, when she was rambling on and the other girls said she was not making sense. She had said that all Renaissance artists were inspired by the Neo-Platonic belief that the soul rises to enlightenment by the progressively rarified experience of the beautiful.

Michelangelo seemed to echo those words when he wrote:

My eyes, longing for beautiful things,
together with my soul longing for salvation,
have no other power
to ascend to heaven
than the contemplation of beautiful things.

The Michelangelo book said that he was influenced by Ficino, and the Neo-Platonist, Plotinus. I found a book called *The Enneads* by Plotinus, and read bits and pieces, I even quickly memorised one quote that I loved,

This is the spirit
Beauty must induce
wonderment
and a delicious trouble
longing and love
and a trembling that is all delight.

But like Carol and her chocolates, I felt compelled to move on, to try something new. I was in the section on philosophy and religion, and a little book by W.B. Yeats on the same shelf caught my eye. I suppose it was the familiar name that made me pick it up. The foreword inside explained that this was his translation of Indian religious writings. I dropped the book like a hot brick, back to its shelf, and was wandering off to the biology section, when once more I found myself looking at myself!

"Now wait a minute," I said to me. "That was prejudice! If you had at least read one page of the actual book, then you would be treating it like any other books, but by not reading ANY of it you were being prejudiced against another race." So I went back to read just one page; to prove to myself that I was not prejudiced! I had become very touchy about this matter of prejudice!

The book started with "The Eesha Upanishad"

That is perfect. This is perfect. Perfect comes from perfect.
Take perfect from perfect, the remainder is perfect.
May peace and peace and peace be everywhere.

"What a lot of rot! Stuff and nonsense! Absolute pollywobble!" I must have said that out aloud, however softly, because a grey-bearded man reading at a table nearby scowled at me.

How can anything be perfect in this world, I thought. I had just been reading, in gory detail, for my project, about the Inquisition and people being tortured and burned at the stake, even during what I had thought was the enlightened, tolerant Renaissance.

Recent stuff is much worse. In my short lifetime there has been an unimaginably awful war. Now more and more stories and photographs are coming to light every day about the unspeakable cruelty in the concentration camps, Japanese and German and Russian, the awful things that happened to Jewish children, all sorts of children, in the war. The world is still teeming with suffering refugees and starving orphans. Even after Hiroshima, which one would think, would stop all testing, make people recoil in horror at the monster they had invented, they go on. We saw an art exhibition, huge black and white and red drawings of the aftermath of the bombs in Japan, and I could hardly look at them. The hydrogen bomb was exploded last year by both America and Russia, and even Britain is testing atomic bombs in Australia. Can you imagine anything more crazy? The world is cruel and crazy and evil, not perfect, I thought indignantly, about to thrust the silly book back on the shelf in disgust for the second time.

Then I flashed back, for the first time in months and months, as I am transported back right now, with my stone in my hand, to a completely different way of seeing the world, to the roots of my life in Africa. Before I opened that book in the library, I had for months thrust all such thought from my mind, concentrating on my material life, my new friends. With the recollection came the dawning realisation that the book was saying more or less what the little child that I had been, had said over and over again. What the old Bushman had said. How fervently I believed in those days that everything was good and right and part of life. I remember when I first returned to the farm from London thinking that not only was everything I was seeing there perfect, but it had even been perfect that Miss Ashburn was cruel, and that the boys had taunted and bullied me, and that even my asthma attacks were part of the perfection, because without all of these things I would not have had the determination and the leverage with my father to return to the farm.

How often, in those faraway days, I found welling up through me the exclamation,

"Everything, every little thing in the world is perfectly beautiful!" That is the way I thought back then. Yet now I don't.

I turned back to the first page of the book in my hand.

The next paragraph had two short sentences.

"Claim nothing. Enjoy."

Once more, at first that seemed stupid. The two short sentences seemed to contradict each other. How could one enjoy life if one had nothing?

Yet having opened the floodgates of memory, strange new thoughts, or old, long-forgotten thoughts seen in new light, came flooding back. I thought in my old way, not my recent way of almost feeling sorry for them, about my little friends in the mountains. They were so different from my present-day friends all wrapped up in expensive material pleasures, always wanting what "everyone else" had, or wanting to outdo everyone else. And I am as bad as "everyone else." Worse probably! Just that day, when we were in the city, my mother wanted to buy me some strong, sensible, white sandals, a little girl style with a strap across the instep, and a buckle.

"No, no!" I had protested, producing a page of shoes in the magazine, *Seventeen,* and pointing to a bone, patent leather sling-back. "Everyone in our group is getting shoes like this this summer. Even Heather. You can ask her mother." The plain truth was that at that time ONLY Heather had those shoes though we all wanted them. And a further truth was that I wanted, in our group, the image of fashion leader rather than fashion follower. Of course it now IS true that once Heather and I started the trend, everyone, absolutely everyone in our group has shoes like that.

My brown friends in Africa had nothing, claimed nothing.

They had no clothes. If they wore woollen jerseys for the couple of coldest months in winter, they took them from the common pile that

Gran had given Dinah, of hand-me-downs and the excess output of the compulsive knitting of the two old aunts. When warmer weather arrived, they shed the jerseys like snakes shedding their unwanted skin, and the way snakes emerge all shiny and bright in their under skin, they delighted in their shiny brown bodies, emerging from the dirty wool.

They had no shoes. They did not envy me my shoes, instead I envied them the tough soles of their feet. Every summer I tried to shed my shoes, to go barefooted, and every summer they laughed at my first tentative forays out on to the gravel on my shoe-tender pink soles. Even Kay and John laughed at my tender feet. They had gone barefooted all the time when they were very young, they said. In the depression the older two had to have shoes for boarding school, but the two of them, still on the farm, had no shoes. By the end of the summer my feet had toughened up; but not much. One could tell when we got thorns in our feet. Dinah used to dig the thorns out with a needle. My feet always bled, because the thorns penetrated into the flesh, but in the thick soles of all the other children, there was seldom bleeding.

If I had offered my shoes to any of those children in those days, they would have said, "Who wants to be bothered with finding shoes in the morning? Who wants to be bothered with shoelaces and buckles? Our soles grow with us, and never wear out. We do not have to find them in the morning. Would you offer shoes to the mountain leopard? Would you put shoes on the mountain baboon? No! We, the fleet of foot have no need of shoes!"

They had no toys. So many games to play, but no toys. Only one or two of their games needed things, like ropes, or knucklebones, and these did not seem to belong to anyone in particular. We made clay oxen to play with, but while I kept one of mine, claimed it when my uncle said all those interesting things about it, and still treasure it, even today, wrapped in cotton wool, they never claimed theirs. Usually we made them, played with them for a while a few days later, and then let them crumble back into the earth. I suppose it was really much more fun making them than playing with them afterwards.

So, why did they never seem to feel sorry for themselves, the way we feel sorry for ourselves when "everybody else" has the latest expensive novelty, and we do not, I wondered. Why did they seem so happy?

Because in their world they had everything! They had the whole wide world. They had those majestic mountains, the best adventure playground on earth. They had their beautiful bodies, and their energy and their awareness and openness to everything around them. In the mornings, they had the sun which always, winter and summer, rose just minutes after they awoke, and was there for them, to warm them, and light their day the minute they emerged from the dark caverns of their huts. Because on that farm we all lived by the rhythm of the rising and setting of the sun, not the tyranny of the clock. On storytelling nights they had the moon, and the stars to stagelight the performance of the storytellers.

In summer the clouds performed for them, rolling and tumbling in from the distant sea, striking delicious fear into their hearts with awe-inspring sound and light displays, with deafening thunderclaps, and fireworks of forked lightning, all especially for their entertainment. What fun to be frightened and awestruck, and amazed and delighted all in one. Then came the icy summer rain, pelting down, deliciously, sensuously cool against hot dusty bodies, cascading into outstretched hands so they could enjoy the deliciously cold drink that came down especially for them from the skies.

"No wonder they always seemed so happy," I thought to myself, suddenly seeing in a clear light of understanding, what I had only vaguely wondered at before. "They claimed nothing and enjoyed everything!"

Even rain, which to my new friends is just a dreary nuisance, to them was an event, a cosmic performance, a gift of the universe.

In the library I knew I was running out of time so I looked down again at the first page of the book in my hand. The last words at the bottom of the page were:

Of a certainty, the man who can see all creatures in himself, himself in all creatures, knows no sorrow. How can a wise man, knowing the unity of life, seeing all creatures in himself, be deluded or sorrowful?

Again, echoes of thoughts, echoes of experiences, echoes of things I do not really understand. It sounded so similar to what the old Bushman had told Dinah. How strange the way certain themes and ideas occur, disappear, then recur in life. Like a beautiful recurring pattern, like sculpture, like music.

I wanted to read on, but when I glanced up I saw my mother at the library desk, so, I put the book back into the shelf and went to gather up my things.

In the days that followed I sometimes wondered about the Indian book that Yeats had translated.

I tried to ask my father about it. He is amazing when I ask him about science, or the war. He seems to know everything. But he seemed vague and judgmental about what he called "those pagan cults".

My mother added, "You don't want to get sucked into any of that nonsense."

I could, in a way, understand her fear. One of her friends has a son called Sebastian. I used to get sick of hearing about Sebastian. How charming he was, how clever, what a stunning fiancée he had. Then three months before the wedding Sebastian went to India to visit a friend he had made at university; a last little bachelor fling before he settled down. When he returned he had "changed". He was "strange". The first shock was at the dinner party his mother gave for his return. She had cooked a traditional English roast beef, the biggest and best roast beef anyone had seen since the war. Sebastian refused, in front of everyone, to even taste it. He had, he said, become a vegetarian. And his hair was long, right down below his earlobes! Then he told his fiancée that he did not want to marry her, told her father that he no longer wanted the job in the firm, said he felt compelled to go back to India to learn yoga and meditation.

"How awful for his mother!"

"Such a crying shame!"

"What a waste!"

"He had such a brilliant future ahead of him."

"What a terrible, terrible embarrassment for his mother."

"Isn't it awful the way these strange cults and pagan religions brainwash our gullible youth." They were the kinds of remarks that I overheard amongst my mother's friends. It was probably why I at first dropped the Indian religious book like a hot brick in the library. It also meant that no one would explain away my curiosity.

I know who might know, I thought one day at school, as I looked across the playground and saw Silvia Hammond, the girl who had done the wonderful painting which did not win a prize, the girl who was always running away from the boarding house, and trying to stow away to India. She was sitting by herself as usual, in the far corner of the grounds, reading a book. I walked over to her instead of joining my circle of friends, even though I felt my circle of friends curiously watching me.

"Hello," I said.

"Hello."

She looked at me penetratingly for a second, and then turned back to her book. I felt rebuffed, as I had the last time I had spoken to her, and was tempted to retreat then and there, back to the safe haven of my group, but I pressed on, "Can you tell me anything about Indian religion?"

"No."

"Oh." This was more than a body language rebuff, this was a very blunt, verbal rebuff. Retreat seemed the only option, yet stubbornly I persisted. "Why not?"

"Because, as my father says, you cannot explain the unexplainable." She sighed deeply at having to state the obvious.

Another dead end. I stood silently for a while trying to get around that rebuff.

"I read a book in a library the other day. It started with: "That is perfect, this is perfect...""

"... 'Perfect comes from perfect. Take perfect from perfect and the remainder is perfect. May peace and peace and peace be everywhere', The Eesha Upanishad from the Ten Upanishads," she interrupted me, and for the first time she smiled.

"What are they? Are they like the Ten Commandments?" I asked.

"You should hear my father on the Ten Commandments!" she laughed. "No it is a collection of words of wisdom from very ancient Indian mystics. You would have read the translation by the poet W.B. Yeats?"

"Yes," I said, and then because it seemed that she was not going to go on, I changed my tack. "Tell me about your father." She had mentioned her father twice in our short conversation, and each time her face had softened.

"He is an architect, he works in India. He designed some great buildings for the British there, and still works for the Indian government. At the moment he is assisting with the building of Chandigarh, a modern city designed by the famous architect Le Corbusier. But he really prefers traditional Indian architecture and sculpture."

"Sculpture!" I exclaimed, despite myself. "What's it like?" I asked eagerly, forgetting for a moment that I had decided to dismiss all thought of sculpture from my mind. "What is Indian sculpture like?"

"My dear child, it would blow your mind. It would shock the socks off your sheltered, English, Christian mind!"

"Oh," I said. I am not, as you can see, a great conversationalist beyond the one-liner witticisms I have cultivated to impress my friends. I mean "Oh" is a dead end to serious dialogue. Even if I had just said "Oh?" in the right tone of voice, with a little upward inflection it would have sounded more sophisticated. So I fell back to my fallback word which had so exasperated John. "Why?"

"Well, in the first place many of the sculptures are nude. Naked men and women, swaying, dancing..."

"I saw lots of real live naked people, dancing and swaying in Africa, so why would I be the least bit shocked by stone nudes?" I interrupted haughtily, trying to salvage some cool sophistication.

"Naked men and women in all sorts of erotic, sexual activities," she continued as though she had not been interrupted.

This time I had the grace to blush. I tried my hardest not to, but of course the harder one tries not to blush, the more one feels heat suffusing the face.

Silvia smiled triumphantly.

"Have you seen these sculptures?" I asked, wanting her to go on, to think about her own thoughts and not about my blushing.

"Well, there are not many left in the north of India where we live, they have all been destroyed by the Moguls; but last year when I was home for the holidays, my father and a Professor Leach, and his wife, and I went on an expedition to look at sculptures. We went to the Chitragupta Temple at Khajuraho and to several other ruined temples in the jungles that practically no one knows about.

When I first saw some of those erotic scenes I couldn't help myself blushing red as a beetroot," she grinned. And I realised that when she had smiled at me, when I had blushed, it had not been a smile of triumph at all, but a smile of sympathy.

"You too?" I laughed in relief.

"Yes. While the grey-haired professor's wife, who must be at least fifty, and one would think all Victorian and narrowminded, did not bat an eyelid, and went on chatting away, saying things like, 'in the Indian mystique, the physical union between two people symbolises a pantheistic act that leads to communion with the universal harmony,' I was blushing speechless! Why is it," she mused, "that at our age, we find ourselves blushing at the least mention of sex, yet I know that if I had seen those same scenes when I was a child, I would not have turned a hair."

"Nor would I have, when I was a child on an African farm," I agreed.

"It must be something that society drums into us as we reach our teens," she said, "or our hormones! But, in India at least I soon got used to the sculptures. I saw so many of them, that I could just enjoy their beauty and vitality without blushing any more. You wouldn't believe some of those temples, teeming all over with people, animal and plants."

"Did you see the Taj Mahal?" I asked. It was the only Indian building I could think of.

"Yes, But of course it is very different from all the other temples I am talking about, there is not a single animal or figure in painting or sculpture anywhere on it, because it was built by a Muslim and the

Islamic religion forbids the depiction of any living thing."

"Oh?" I said.

"So of course do the Jewish and Christian religions. The second commandment," she went on.

"Thou shalt not make unto thee any graven image, or any likeness of any thing that is in the heaven above, or that is in the earth beneath or that is in the water under the earth," I quoted.

I remembered, but of course did not tell Silvia, how reading that for the first time seemed like another blow to my little childhood dream of being a sculptor. I mean it is bad enough when one's parents dismissively pooh-pooh the idea, or when one's headmistress says what a ridiculous notion, but when God himself heaves in with a hefty, "thou shalt NOT" how can such a fragile dream stand a chance?

"My father says that commandment has been responsible for more violence and vandalism and wanton destruction of sacred art than anything else in the world. All those Hindu, Jain and Buddhist temples and sculptures destroyed in India, and in Europe all that Greek art destroyed by the Christians. Even quite recently in England the Protestants went around vandalising hundreds and hundreds of church sculptures in England, feeling all self-righteous about themselves. My father went around England last time he was here with Professor Leach, looking at some little known fragments of the work of an English sculptor whose work was all destroyed in his lifetime. My father was really upset by what he saw; he said the man must have been as great a sculptor as Michelangelo! Imagine having a lifetime's work just smashed to pieces in the name of religion! But I suppose if he wanted to be a sculptor he had to take that risk."

"Would you?"

"Would I what?"

"Take the risk? Be a sculptor?"

"Not on your life! Sculptors have to risk derision because they have to put their work out there in public. Even today you would be exposing yourself to all sorts of Philistines!"

"But you will be an artist?" I persisted.

"Oh yes! I have worked it all out. I am going to be a poet painter, and a painter poet."

Just then the bell rang.

"Darn!" I exclaimed, "Now we have to go to boring old House Meetings."

These assemblies are excruciatingly boring. Morning prayer is nice, a hymn, a prayer and a recessional which we keep singing as we march all the way from the chapel to the classrooms, but once a week, after break we have House Meetings.

All of us have to belong to a "house" (my house is called Thomas) and we are supposed to have something called "house spirit", so we are harangued about school rules and school spirit, and then all the team captains tell the results of all the sports matches, and then we are exhorted to participate in, or at least barrack for, all next week's sports.

We can earn "house marks" for our house by playing in winning teams, or doing charitable work, or being dux, but we can also "lose" house marks for various misdemeanours. One of the silliest is for spilling ink, because at our school we still have to use calligraphy pens, dipped into little inkwells, set into our desks.

At these house meetings all the miscreants, who have lost a house-mark in the past week, have to line up, in front of the whole house, and apologise. Once, when I had spilt some ink, and had to join the guilty lineup, I listened to each of the other offenders say "Sorry Thomas", one after the other.

"Sorry Thomas!" "Sorry Thomas!" "Sorry Thomas!" they intoned, some genuinely contrite, most simply trying hard to sound terribly contrite. I got the giggles. Now this is meant to be a solemn and serious business, but the more I tried to regain my composure, the more I was shaken with uncontrollable laughter, until my turn came and I tried to start: "So…sor… sorreeee," and I just collapsed into peals of giggling laughter. A few nervous types sniggered, but most of the prefects who run these meetings glared stonily. So you can see why I don't particularly like house meetings.

"We don't HAVE to go," said Silvia. "That's why I sit way down here, by myself on Thursdays. As soon as everyone else has their back turned, walking towards the hall, I duck into that clump of hedges and shrubs. You can stay with me if you like."

"I'd better not," I started to think, then suddenly felt that old urge to thumb my nose at authority, with its silly rules and regulations, and I nodded my head.

"You haven't lost a house mark this week have you?" I shook my head.

"Well then, nobody will notice that we are missing," she said, grabbing my arm and dragging me around the hedge into what seemed like a little green cave, its ceiling a multitude of different shades of green and different shaped leaves.

We sat there, close together, hugging our knees, my heart pounding at the thought of being discovered, Silvia with the nonchalance of someone who had done this before.

"Keep dead still for a few minutes," she whispered. "In case the teacher on playground duty comes around."

Before, as we talked, I had stood apart from Silvia, space and strangeness separating us. Now we were huddled so closely together that although we were not touching I could feel the warmth of her body along one side, contrasting with the cool of the dank earth beneath me, and the cool of the slight breeze brushing my cheeks. When we turned to face each other our eyes were so close together that I could see the flecks of green-gold in her green-blue eyes, echoing the flecks of gold in her bright red hair. She winked and grinned.

I was still nervous, alert, straining my ears to hear any approaching teacher's footsteps, or my friends looking for me, hearing only silence, and the occasional twittering of sparrows in distant trees, so the rousing introductory notes of the School Song on the piano, and the hearty voices of the girls chiming in, seemed unusually loud.

"There now, we can talk as loudly as we want to," laughed Silvia.

I could not help still whispering, "Go on, tell me about your plans as painter poet."

"Well, you know William Blake?"

Tiger, tiger burning bright,
  in the darkness of the night ...

I quoted.

"Yes well, he wrote poetry and painted strange paintings to go with it, and published it in books that were partly printed, and partly hand painted. Well, that is what I am going to do, so that my art will only be seen and owned by genuine art lovers. Like Blake I am going to do all the printing and binding and publishing myself." She went on talking excitedly, telling me about her plans for the illustrations which would be inspired not only by Blake, but by modern Surrealist painters, and Chagall and Klee, and her poetry which would be inspired by Keats and Shelley and T.S. Eliot, while I marvelled at how much she knew, and how widely she read.

She went on, "I think all art should in some way transcend the boundaries of the inner and outer life, and so what I would really really like to try to do, is mix into my poems some Indian mystical thought.

Did you know that they don't believe in one God, that old man with a beard, sitting up there judging us all. Instead they believe in Consciousness. A universal Consciousness that is in every single thing, and our individual Consciousness is part of that universal Consciousness. Sometimes it is called something else, like the Absolute, or the Self, but it means the same. Our individual selves are not separate, but part of the Universal Self. Do you see what I mean?"

"I don't even know what my personal self is," I admitted, "What am I? Who am I? Am I my body, or my mind, or my personality?"

"None of those," answered Silvia emphatically. "A body changes all the time, new cells every day. My body even looks different every year. A few years ago I had a tomboy child's body, now I have the body of a woman. Your personality changes all the time too, and besides it is only a mask. Personality comes from the Greek word *persona*, or mask. Your mind is closer, but you change your mind, thoughts come and go; and you can watch your mind, stand aside and observe your own mind working. Now THAT'S your real self, that part of you that is the watcher, the observer, the witness. And that is the part that is one with the whole universe!"

She seemed fired with enthusiasm, or perhaps, she was just answering my original question. Then suddenly her voice flattened.

"You probably think I am a nut-case. The girls in my class tell me, straight to my face, that I am crazy, off my rocker, weird, strange, if ever I get carried away and find myself mentioning anything like this. Sorry to bore you, especially as I have you captive for the duration of assembly. Bet you'd rather be listening to the hockey results than some loony."

"No! No of course not, just the opposite. I am terribly interested. It is funny how I also, throughout my life, keep coming upon ideas about oneness, unity. In Africa, the old Bushman used to say that we are all one with the earth and the animals and the stars and the sky. We are studying the Renaissance in History and some men then suggested something similar. But strangest of all, my father is very interested in science, and he often brings me new articles in journals to read. My mother keeps telling him that it is above my head, and of course she is right, but I read them anyhow. One article was about the implications of Quantum Physics, and amongst all the scientific jargon that seemed to suggest that time and space, waves and particles are all inter-related and interchangeable there were these two funny sentences that I memorised. One scientist wrote, 'When a butterfly flutters its wings, the vibrations are felt on the other side of the world.' Another, a Nobel prizewinner, said 'If you tickle the universe here, it laughs over there.' How odd, I thought. How Very, Very Odd. Those words came from Very Clever Scientists, so they must Mean Something."

Silvia giggled. "You are talking with capital letters like Winnie the Pooh!"

"How do you know?"

"I just know! So, did you find any deep and meaningful Meaning?"

Yes!" I exclaimed, feeling exhilarated at being able to talk to Silvia like this.

"Like a flash of white light I suddenly realised that the Very Clever scientists were saying more or less what the Very Wise old Bushman said. That is my theory anyhow!"

"That is your trouble," said Silvia, "Too theoretical! Too clever! All that really matters is simple experience. What about your own personal experience? Feeling? Do you ever actually feel oneness with everybody else?"

"No," I had to admit, shaking my head sadly. "Most of the time I feel just the opposite; separation, loneliness, isolation. Like an island all by myself."

"So do I, obviously, because I spend most of my time by myself, but that is strange coming from you. You are popular, an insider, in the inner circle of a super groovy crowd. I have watched you, always right in the middle of a group that thinks it is the bee's knees."

"Look Silvia, there is sometimes nothing lonelier than a crowd. I have stood, all alone, in high mountains, with not a single soul in sight, and not felt a bit lonely, yet sometimes, in my super groovy crowd, as you call it, when we are all shrieking and freaking, discussing movie star gossip, or our own gossip, being catty, because our group makes an art of being catty, of witty put downs and denigration of anyone who is the slightest bit eccentric or different or just not groovy, I often have this strong feeling of not belonging, of what am I doing here, I'd rather be having a serious conversation with one of those oddities we're mocking."

"Like me?" she smiled wryly.

I made a funny face, and nodded.

"On the other hand, the trouble is," I went on, "I consciously cultivate the girls in my group, I copy them, ape them, emulate their behaviour, even outdo them, I can be wittier and snootier than the best of them, then I excuse myself to myself by saying it is all a game. Because being part of that group is a safe, snobby feeling. The thought of actually in real life going off by myself in the playground and reading a book, being seen to be alone, the way you do, fills me with terror and dread. I know this will sound silly to you, but I would rather die, than have to be seen alone in the playground."

"You'll learn! You just have to be quite detached. Just imagine you are alone on your mountain. You mentioned being all alone on a high mountain earlier, tell me about it."

So I told her about the day I climbed to the high peak, leaving my friends enjoying their sweets, about finding the Bushman cave, about being transfixed by the beautiful painting of the Eland, and finding the

Bushman stone, thinking it was a gift of the spirit, feeling my being expanding, feeling one with the mountains, seeing the eagle, flying with the eagle.

"I was only eight years old at the time," I concluded almost by way of an apology, an excuse, "I supposed one fantasises a lot when one is small."

Despite the camaraderie of huddling together illicitly in a hedge, I felt embarrassed about telling such a story, and quickly went on to tell Silvia about my African friends. How they were perfect examples of young people who claimed nothing and yet enjoyed life to the full.

"The trouble is," she mused when I told her about their disdain for shoes, their saying "Would you give shoes to the mountain leopard?"

"The trouble is, one day, some capitalist exploiter is going to convince just one of your young friends that he or she needs shoes to be happy. Then it will not be long before they all want them, when they will all begin to think that they need shoes to be happy."

"But lets go back to that experience of yours in the mountains. The amazing thing is that I was about eight or nine too when I had a similar experience. Something I have never forgotten."

"Tell me about it."

"We had only been in India for a year or two, and during a very hot summer we went for a week's holiday to a lovely old-fashioned hotel up in the mountains and lakes of Kashmir. At that time an Indian woman was my sort of *ayah* or governess. I called her Ananda, though that was only part of her long name. At home she only came in during the day, but when we went on this holiday she came with us, and stayed in my room at the hotel. Her job was to keep an eye on me, and entertain me, take me for walks and that sort of thing. Every morning, when I woke up, she would be sitting in the windowsill, cross legged. When I asked her what she was doing she answered that she had been meditating, but she always stopped as soon as I awoke, and we would go out for wonderful long walks along the banks of the lake in the cool of the morning, only coming back for breakfast when everybody else was having morning tea. On the last morning of the holidays I awoke in the dark, before dawn, before Ananda. I was up and dressed by the time she awoke, and excitedly told her that I wanted to be down by the lake to watch the sun rise.

I can't describe what an exquisite morning it was, the mountains, the lake, the wisps of mist, the sunrise, and I was quite delirious with exhilaration! Even then I felt as light and wispy and beautiful as the veil of mist. We ran, Ananda and I, and laughed, and did cartwheels in the dewy grass, and splashed icy water on our hot faces. Then after a while Ananda said, "Come Silvia, we must sit quietly now. I missed my meditation this morning. I must meditate now."

I was a restless, overactive child, and I resisted, saying no, she could sit, I would go on chasing butterflies. But she insisted, and made me sit cross legged on the grassy bank besides her. But still I was restless and fidgety. "Be still. Be still, Silvia," she said, "Look at the reflections in the lake. It is only because the lake is quite, quite still that it is able to reflect everything else in itself."

When I really looked I was amazed to see that the reflections of the mountains mirrored in the lake were almost more vivid than the mountains themselves. I found myself really concentrating on those reflections in the lake, trying to distinguish them from the real images. Once a slight breeze ruffled the surface for a moment, and immediately the reflections lost their clarity, and became chaotic and blurred. Then the lake fell still again, quite quite still, and the mirrored mountains once more became clearer in the lake than they were in the air. And I too fell into a deep stillness like the lake. And then I became the lake, and the whole world was reflected in me, and I became the whole world. In that utter stillness I felt that the whole world was reflected in my being.

When I told Ananda about it afterwards, she seemed delighted.

"Goodness gracious me! Goodness gracious me! That is verry, verry good!"

Yet when I tried to tell my parents at dinner they seemed anxious and disturbed. When we returned home Ananda was dismissed. My mother in particular seemed nervous about what she called pagan cults. Of course that was seven years ago, and since then my father has become interested in Indian art and the transcendental thinking behind the art. When we went on that safari last year, searching out old temples in the jungle, there was nothing else to do in the evenings but talk, and the grown-ups talked for hours with me listening silently. Mrs Leach was so knowledgeable, she had grown up in India, and she knew the Upanishads and the "Geeta" off by heart. Quoted quietly in the firelight they sounded beautiful to me. That is why I recognised your quote.

"Which," she went on in a less dreamy voice, "brings me to a secret I want to tell you. I am not going to tell anyone else, except of course the headmistress who has to know.

"You know how much I want to go back to India. You must know, everybody knows about those melodramatic attempts to run away, and stow away on a ship to India! When I realised the futility of that strategy I started writing my parents letters that made this school sound worse that a Charles Dickens orphanage! Perhaps I exaggerated too much because the only response I got was a rather stern letter from my mother saying that she and my father were adamant that I should finish my education in England. I had pretty well resigned myself to sticking it out, and wrote wooden, banal letters home from then on. Then a couple of weeks ago in letter writing prep, I found myself writing to my father, telling him about my harvester painting. How it started as an ordinary school exercise, a group of three women with scythes cutting wheat. I think the scythes were a little marxist touch to annoy my teacher! But as I worked on it, the painting, by itself seemed to want to transcend the ordinary, and I did it over and over again, not larger and more complex, but smaller and simpler, until I felt that the harvest and the harvesters became one, the rhythms of the waving wheat and the rhythms of the swinging scythes became one, until the whole picture was a little microcosm of the unity of the universe. But when I gave it to the art teacher to enter into the Arts festival she looked at it and all she said was, 'oh, alright,' and then, when I went to the opening of the exhibition, there it was, hanging at the end of the hall, far from the winners and the good ones.

"'The next day at break,' I wrote, 'this skinny little kid in the class below me, one of the prizewinners, came across the playground towards me. I watched her coming and watched her friends watching her, and thought, it must take a lot of courage to walk across the playground toward me in front of that lot, because all the girls here think I am weird. Actually she is also slightly strange, something of a contradiction herself, in one way clever, and always winning prizes and dux of her year, and yet she stupidly hangs about with a group of silly little girls who think they are so super cool but really they are just frivolous and superficial. Anyhow she came up to me, and said that the judges had got it all wrong, that my painting should have won.

"'I was so shocked and surprised and overwhelmed that she should not only think it, recognise what I had done, but also come over and tell me, that I went to pieces. I felt tears well up into my eyes, and spill down my cheeks. Of course I could not possibly let her see so I turned my back on her and said something terribly rude and hurtful so that she would go away, straight away.'"

Silvia stopped quoting her letter and lapsed into silence, and I could not say anything, not even my feeble "oh" because I too had a frog in my throat.

Just then the school piano broke into a recessional march, to signal that House Meetings were to end, girls began were spilling out into the playground, marching off to their lessons; and this galvanised Silvia in to finishing her story.

"That's all I wrote. I just signed my initial, and shoved it in the envelope. But something in that letter must have struck a cord with my father, because, as soon as he got it he wired me. The long and the short of it is that Mrs Leach, the professor's wife is in England and she is going to escort me home. So that is my secret," she smiled happily, "I am leaving for India in three days time. And somehow, in some way, you had something to do with it!"

"That is wonderful!" I exclaimed, yet feeling my heart sink at the thought of losing this new friend so soon.

She must have read my thoughts because she said, "I'll write to you! I'll write care of the school! One day, someplace I absolutely know that both of us will reflect the mountains in our beings again. And we will be able to tell each other without feeling foolish!"

"It's no good! " I cried, "I will be leaving too, at the end of term. And I have no idea what my address will be."

"To Africa?" she exclaimed excitedly.

"No. We are going to Australia."

"You poor thing! Now that, I hear, is really and truly a land of Philistines!"

CHAPTER FIFTEEN

MEN-AN-TOL OR THE STONE-WITH-A-HOLE

"In ALL ranks of life, the human heart

yearns for the beautiful."

HARRIET BEECHER STOWE

A week before my own birthday, my fourteenth, I dreamed that I was an eagle again. An eagle searching the earth, scouring the whole world for a talisman, for a gift of certitude.

After a while, I realised in my dream that what I was looking for was my long lost Bushman stone. All night I flew and flew, all over the world, flapping my wings, at first effortlessly, swooping and gliding, and then more and more frantically, straining at wings that became heavier and heavier, until my shoulders and my chest ached, as I became more and more desperate. At last I was so exhausted, and the wings so heavy, and I was flying so slowly, that I could barely keep from scraping the ground. Yet I could not stop searching for my stone, though I knew it was a hopeless quest.

The next morning at breakfast when my father asked me what I wanted to do for my birthday, without even having thought about it I said I would like to drive down to Cornwall, before we left for Australia, to find the Men-an-Tol, the ancient Stone-with-a-hole. My parents were both quite taken aback, what on earth for, they both asked, but there did not seem much point in telling them that one of the aunts on the farm had talked about it, had compared it with my Bushman stone. I was simply adamant that that was all I wanted for my birthday. Mother of course wanted to give me a party. Why not both, suggested my father, suddenly capitulating. My parents are wonderful in that way, they will indulge my slightest whim as far as birthday treats and outings are concerned. I could tell that my mother was not at all keen on the trip, she thought it would be far too boring for my young brother for one weekend, and so I felt desperately grateful when she agreed to go.

The weekend of my birthday arrived, and on Saturday, after a quick visit to the hospital to see the patients he had operated on the day before, Father piled us into the car and we set out right across England; the distances so small compared with Africa, that we could do it in one day. We arrived at St Ives just as the sun was setting in the west, over the Atlantic Ocean.

The hotel owner had never heard of the Men-an-Tol, but offered as consolation the information that there were some artists working in St Ives, including a sculptor-lady with triplets. I pricked up my ears at this, but Father said we were not the least bit interested in the artists' colony, only archeology, only the Men-an-tol. Eventually he found someone who said that it was between the villages of Morvah and Madron.

"We'll enquire there in the morning," said Father.

Then the next morning, my birthday, when we awoke, St Ives was shrouded in mist. Neither the wispy white mist of my mountains, nor the ghastly grey fog of London but an opaque, impenetrable surging white blanket rolling and tumbling in from the Atlantic.

"Well that's that then," sighed Mother, "we can't possibly go trapsing over the moors in this!" Father being a man of action was not so easily deterred, so he and I set out in the car for Morvah. There, it was difficult to find anyone about, and more difficult to find anyone who would tell us where to find the stone.

"Why not go and see Lanyon Quoit instead," grumbled an old man who seemed to know. "It be near a road and easy to find. Like a small Stonehenge, very popular with tourists."

"I am not a tourist! I must find Men-an-Tol!" I must have said with such passion and desperation that the old man looked at me piercingly, his face close to mine, as though the better to see it through the fog.

Then suddenly he took the map in my hand, and made an X on it. "It be there. Car can only drive to here," he made another mark on the map. "Then ye'll be walking."

The mist seemed, if that were possible, to thicken, but the road was so narrow that we could use the thick stone walls on either side, so close that the outside mirrors kept scraping against them, to guide us. By the time we left the car, and had clamoured over an old stile, over a crumbling stone wall, and set out across the gorse and heather, using the compass my father had had the foresight to bring, we could hardly see a foot ahead. Once a dark ghostly form loomed out of the mist, but it was only the ruin of an ancient tin mine, said Father. On we went, stumbling through thickets of gorse, becoming soaking wet when we fell into shrubs, invisible until we stumbled into them, until even Father's determination began to waiver, and he suggested that we had come out on a wild goose chase, that we could never, ever find anything in this silent white world.

I pretended not to hear, and hurried off ahead of him, as fast as I could, terrified that I would once again feel his hand grasp my shoulder, turning me around, back to the car. When I heard him call me, I started running with a kind of blind, white desperation, desperate to keep ahead, out of earshot, out of reach.

I was so intent on keeping out of reach, pushing blindly into the whiteness, that the sudden clearing in the mist caught me by surprise, and I stopped, struck stock still.

There in front of me was a circular clearing in the white world, a shaft of sunlight spearing down, a prism of mist particles shimmering in the rays; and there, under the spear of sunlight was the Stone-with-a-Hole.

Slowly I advanced towards it, my hands outstretched like a sleepwalker, half expecting to find that I was seeing a mirage, that would dissolve back into the mist as I approached. Then I was touching it, running my hands around the stone, caressing my cheek against the cool, lichen-covered surfaces, feeling the almost circular outer edge, and running my hands around the perfectly circular inner void, revelling in the lovely, starkly simple shape.

"It is so beautiful," I whispered to myself, and suddenly I was back in a mountain landscape so different to this flat moor, holding a small stone not all that very different in shape from this large Men-an-Tol, which seemed to be resonating with the same energy, filling me with the same sense of expanding, and becoming one with the universe.

Then Father stumbled up and broke the magic silence with his exclamation of triumph.

"We found it! See how accurate a compass can be, if one knows how to use it properly." Then he started propounding the theories about the origin of the stone, the pre-Druidic religious rites that were thought to have taken place here, explaining about the two upright dolmens on either side of the Men-an-tol, which I had not, until then, even noticed. For once I did not want to listen to his encyclopaedic information, for once I wanted only to listen to the humming of the stone against the background silence of the universe.

By the time we returned to the car the mist had dissolved, become thin and wispy like my mountain mist, and by the time we reached St Ives again, to fetch my mother and my little brother from the hotel, the sun was shining.

Halfway home we stopped at a pretty little pub for lunch, and my father, as he sometimes does, chatted with the waitress. It started as a discussion on the relative merits of the Cornish pasties he had had the day before, and the cold pork pie he had just ordered.

"Cornish pasties are nice," she said, "but Cornish double cream fudge is divine."

"Well well well, what a coincidence!" laughed my father, pulling a small box of double cream Cornish fudge from his pocket and offering it to her. "We have just been all the way to Cornwall for a night just so that…" And he used a wry, humorous tone, the kind that expects an incredulous reaction… "Just so that my daughter here could see a stone!!"

Instead of the expected, "whatever for?" reaction, the girl said seriously, "Which stone?"

"The Men-an-Tol."

"The stone with a hole! Well if you are so interested in stones, why not come and see the stone circle near our farmhouse. My father is an archeologist and bought the farm especially to be near the stone circle. I finish my shift here in ten minutes, and you can drive me home."

"Yes, let's go and see the stone circle!" chimed my little brother, most unexpectedly, so we went.

We parked near the farmhouse, and clambered over an old wooden stile, and there, in a green field, in England's green and pleasant land, was a stone circle that bore an uncanny resemblance to a stone circle on that rocky, arid, African mountain. A circular echo.

I was so intrigued by the stones that when the girl's father wandered up and started talking to my father, I remained slightly aside from the group, silent, separate, self-contained.

My father always researches his subjects thoroughly, and was now propounding the theories that he had tried to talk to me about at the Men-an-Tol, the kind of encyclopaedic knowledge I would normally love to listen to.

"What's your theory about the reason for these circles?" he concluded, "a burial site? A temple to their gods? A sacrificial altar? An astrological observatory?"

"Art," said the man. "Sculpture. One fine day modern artists are going to cotton on to the fact that these are sculptures!"

I hurried over to listen more closely.

"But all those thousands of man-hours of labour. There must have been some practical use for them! Some reasonable logic," said my father.

"Art making is not necessarily logical," said the man seriously.

"You mean they just did it, because they did it!" I piped in. "Just because the stones are so beautiful."

The man threw back his head and laughed, then, with a little conspiratorial wink at me, he said, "We understand!"

He was echoing exactly what my brown friends had exclaimed so long ago. Echoes always recur.

The next weekend my mother had her party for my birthday, and for her sake I pretended to enjoy it, to be bright and happy.

Of course Mother never asked me if I were happy but then even if she had, I would have answered dutifully, "Yes Mother, I am happy."

Only Gran, my beloved Gran, who used to understand me, could have understood, would have noticed that once in a while I let the animated smiling mask slip, and I would see reflected in a window, instead of eyes, haunted, black holes of loneliness. Only she, who used to know me so well, could possibly observe that, despite my so-called popularity, there was not the comfortable, easy candour that I had enjoyed with Ethel and Iris. I had used them as sounding boards to some of my more farfetched ideas and feelings; and I believed at the time that they understood everything I said because they always listened so intently, fixing me with liquid dark eyes, making sympathetic murmurs, clicking their tongues in agreement, so that I was never embarrassed or afraid of saying something silly.

I tried to write to Ethel and Iris once. I addressed the letter to the Commissioner for Native Affairs, and wrote a covering letter explaining that I could only write in English, and they could not read at all, but if he could send someone to read it aloud to them they would understand. That was when I was still naive enough to hope for a response. Nothing ever came back from Africa.

Since then, except for that brief magic encounter with Silvia in the hole in the hedge, there has been no one I could really confide in, hardly anyone who would even remotely understand what I must admit are silly longings, out-of-reach aspirations. No matter how bright and cheerful I try to be on the outside, inwardly, I suppose rather like Silvia, I keep my distance, build an invisible protective carapace around my inner self, like the hard, protective shell of my beautiful mountain tortoises.

CHAPTER SIXTEEN

BOTTICELLI HANDS

"The most important thing in living, is to reach out and touch perfection in that which you most love to do."

JONATHAN LIVINGSTON SEAGULL,
RICHARD BACH

One of the things Mother, who knows nothing of my wayward thoughts, feels very strongly about is my piano lessons, and so I try very hard to please her by working hard at my practice.

When I first returned from Africa, she made me rub cream into my brown, calloused hands every night and made me sleep in white cotton gloves which I hated; but soon my strong, rough mountain hands turned soft and white and it was only then that Mother realised what long, sensitive fingers I had.

"Look!" she exclaimed. "You can stretch an octave easily even at your age! You could become a concert pianist," and then she sighed sadly.

"I came to London to study the piano because I wanted to become a concert pianist; but then I married and became pregnant with you!"

I wondered whether I should feel guilty that my existence had prevented my mother from becoming a concert pianist, and so I worked hard to fulfil my mother's ambitions.

But now, at fourteen, I know in my heart that, though I love the music, I do not have anywhere near the talent to be a concert pianist. Sometimes I also wonder whether my mother really and truly wanted to become a concert pianist, or whether it was just something her school and her teachers and her family expected from her because she was so very good at playing the piano. I remember now, once long ago on the farm, something she said to her sister about a concert.

"I was a bundle of nerves, utterly petrified, waiting alone in the wings before the concert. Then suddenly I saw a builder's hammer, a hammer left behind by the stage hands. In a flash I picked it up, and found myself thinking of striking my other hand with that great big hammer, smashing my knuckles, so that I would not be able, could not be made to play with a broken hand!"

Now, as I practise, I sometimes watch in an almost detached way, my hands on the keys and I find myself thinking, as I watch the fingers striking the keys, of my mother thinking of striking her own hand. Of my own hands striking the piano when they would rather be doing something else.

"Those are sculptor's hands, not pianist's hands!" and I try to push such thoughts out of mind.

Long gone are the times when I tentatively and obliquely broached the subject of being a sculptor, because each time the receiver of such a confidence, however veiled, would be so aghast at the very idea, that my determination waned, and then faded like a dream in the harsh light of reality. For a long stretches of time I tried not to think of sculpture at all.

Yet now and then, the thought comes, unbidden into my mind as I watch my fingers on the keyboard.

"Those are sculptor's hands, not pianist's hands. A keyboard is for striking, sculpture is for stroking. My hands are stroking hands not striking hands."

A Bach phrase I sometimes practise seems determined to take up the chant:

Stroking hands not striking hands,
stroking hands not striking hands,
stroking hands not striking hands.

When that happens, I play those bars over and over and over again because my psyche swells at Bach's insight, because I sense, just for a fleeting second, somewhere deep in my suppressed, intuitive soul, that there is a strange kind of rightness about that funny phrase, my hands are sensuous, caressing, stroking hands.

But I have to be sensible, and so at other times I enjoy, with a wry smile to myself, the irony of those words, because people often comment on my hands.

"What striking hands!" they exclaim.

Striking in the other sense of the words, strikingly noticeable, strikingly beautiful, they say.

Recently, one of my music examiners said exactly that, "What striking hands!" and then went on to compare them with the hands of Botticelli's Venus, and his three Graces, in the *Primavera*.

I wanted to ask her more about those paintings but I could not, in the tense little music room.

So afterwards I looked up the Botticelli hands in an art book, and there, in the same book, I found what I decided was a much more apt comparison.

A painting by a sixteenth century Mannerist painter, Parmigianino, a painting popularly known, the book said, as the *Madonna of the Long Neck.* *

I thought it might just as aptly have become known as *The Madonna of the Long Fingers,* because that is what I noticed first about the Madonna, her long sensuous fingers.

For centuries, critics have said those fingers were a Mannerist distortion, Mannerist exaggeration; no human fingers could possibly be that long, that elegant.

I looked down at my own hands; they came uncannily close.

* To view image, go to Google images: Parmigianino. Madonna Long Neck.

CHAPTER SEVENTEEN

THE MYTH OF ETERNAL RETURN

"We shall not cease from exploration
And the end of all our exploring
Will be to arrive where we started
And know the place for the first time."

T. S. ELIOT

I find myself watching those hands now as they put down the rock from the Mountains of the Dragon and unwrap the bull once more from the cotton wool.

It glows, a lusty luminescent red, a deep earthy red, in the last red rays of the setting sun, shafting through my small west-facing window.

The lily-white Botticelli hands are nearly demented with excitement; writhing with nervous energy.

"Weren't we clever?" they seem to be saying to each other.

"We made this. We took a lump of mud, a formless, shapeless lump of clay, and we coaxed it into volumes and forms, planes and curves that positively invite stroking and caressing."

The fingers follow each other along the planes, around the curves, up, over and around again.

"We were so clever," they are saying to each other. "Not only did we make this marvellous tactile object, but we took a meaningless, characterless material and charged it with dynamic energy, with the very essence of vitality and virility."

I smile to myself. When Uncle Ben used the word, virility, so many years ago, I did not really know what it meant.

I know now!

He was right, my little bull is the very essence of virility. No wonder those sensuous, sensual fingers are going mad with excitement.

But wait! They are over-excited, they are going too far! They squeeze too hard, and the tail, that last little whip-snip of contained energy, breaks off in my left hand, while the horns, those upright, pointed symbols of virility, snap off into my right hand.

Contrite, the fingers quiver for a moment, then go still and limp, as the mutilated carcass lies emasculated in the concave curves of trembling white palms.

As I watch, stunned, a heavy tear falls, and trickles, blood red, down its rump. You see, the bull in my hands is made of sun-dried terracotta, not kiln-fired terracotta, so even after all these years, it takes no more than a tear to convert the surface back to blood-red mud.

I keep watching, mesmerised, as a torrent of tears cascades onto the mutilated torso, eroding little rivulets across the planes, dissolving the iron-red clay, until it plops, thick and turgid, ox-blood red, ox-blood consistency, into my palms.

Gradually the little rivulets become a deeply eroded dongas, like the red eroded dongas in the earth itself, and the small bleeding wound a torrent, until at last, the once beautiful form is no more than a shapeless, characterless, lump of mud, and my hands; and the once beautiful lily-white, Botticelli hands, are blood red, ox-blood red.

I stand up, and walk stiffly to the tall, black rubbish bin, with my hands outstretched before me like a sleep-walker.

Then I tilt my hands slowly, slightly. Slowly, sluggishly, the remains of my sculpture slip into the rubbish bin, the way I would imagine human remains (the way I have, to my horror, imagined human remains) sliding slowly into the crematorium hatch.

As my once-beautiful bull slips slowly, inexorably, off my hands, into the blackness of the bin, at the very moment that the sun slips out of the red sky, plunging my whole room into gloom, I experience the same sense of finality, of severance that I had when my beloved mountains slipped from my sight all those years ago.

Mechanically, robot-like, I turn and pick up the rock from the Mountains of the Dragon and commit it too, to the bin. I cannot bury one without the other; the bull of virility and the rock of the Earth-mother have lain so long together in their marriage bed of cotton wool, they belong together; for so long they have symbolised my past and my future; my memories and my dreams; my roots and my aspirations.

They belong together like Gran and my real grandfather. They tried to tell me that Gran died of a heart attack in New Zealand three months ago, but I do not believe them. I know that she died from a broken heart, pining for the farm, pining for Africa. I know because of the way she wrote cheerful vivid letters to me, reminiscing longingly, lovingly about our life in the mountains.

At first I blamed my step-grandfather for taking her to New Zealand, blamed Kay for writing to say how happy they were, how well they had settled in to the sheep farm next to her new New Zealand husband.

Then I heard that my step-grandfather had had Gran cremated, and though I cringed and baulked at the idea of my warm cheerful Gran committed to fire, when I heard that he had made a long and treacherous, storm-fraught sea-voyage, to bury Gran in the magic circle surrounded by the dark phalanx of green cypress pines, I forgave him.

It seems so right that those two are together at last. But my imagination cannot reconcile the young man with the face of a beautiful marble Apollo, with an older woman, over fifty, even a wonderful older woman like Gran. So my imagination has, of its own volition, wound back the clock, so that now the image that fills my mind to bursting point is of Gran as a young girl, strong-willed, courageous, defiant enough to defy her parents, defy society, for the man she loves.

But if that young woman lives so vividly, so vibrantly in my imagination, fills the picture gallery of my head, then there is no room in there for the grandmother I loved, who loved me, the writer of those letters, which is why, today, I have had to commit them all, like ghost butterflies, to the bin.

I recoil back from that bin with a kind of loathing; it has taken so much from me. It becomes a phantom barge on a black sea, receding, taking with it my bull and my stone, wrapped in a shroud of my drawings of bones and skeletons, and my rainbow-kalaidoscope rabbit, and all Gran's letters.

Together.

On a distant phantom island, with a ring of green trees and a sun-shafted inner circle, among beautiful sculptures, I see my achingly handsome, long-dead grandfather, and my vibrantly defiant young grandmother, as beautiful and as joyous as the marble girl striding into the wind, into an opposing force.

Together.

Further into the distance, a small green island with Kay and John and my step-grandfather, and Kay's husband, settled into their New Zealand sheep farm.

Together.

The loveliest vision, of great craggy mountains, jagged and fissured, bleak and bare, of krantzes and cliffs, caves and spires spearing like great cathedrals up into the heavens, is receding faster than the others, floating outwards like the expanding universe, so that I can only just discern Dinah and Ethel and Iris and the grizzled Old Grandfather, with all the others, like black granite statues.

Together.

I stand on a bleak island of my own.

Alone.

Deep down, somewhere in the lost depths of my being, I feel the beginning of a primal scream, a cry of misery, as lonely and miserable as the cry of the last lonely leopardess. Up through my body it rises, rushes, whirls, straining at my aching throat.

There is a myth of eternal return; it says that everything recurs as we once experienced it; that echoes have echoes. *"Das schwerste Gewicht"*, Nietzsche calls it; the heaviest of burdens.

Just as, long, long ago, that long-lost agonising, howling reply to the lone leopardess in the moonlight was bottled back into my throat by the gentle touch of a wizened finger, so this more strident scream is smashed back into my throat by the loud knock on the door, and the cheerful voice of my mother.

The scream shatters, splintered, back into my throat, and the slivers and splinters slide back down into the very depths of my soul, searing, slicing, as they fall.

They cut a hole right through the centre of my being; leaving an empty space, just like the empty space in the centre of my beloved Bushman stone; a void, where my heart and soul should be.

My mother is standing there in the doorway. She is telling me that the woman downstairs has come to take the things for charity.

I square my shoulders, lift my chin, bite into my trembling lower lip and stiffen my upper lip. I look down at my ox-bloodstained hands, and quickly hide them behind my back, so that when Mother steps right into the room, flicks on the electric light, and says, "You have been up here for hours. What have you been doing?" I am able, like a robot, programmed to be sweet and bright, to reply, without the slightest trace of emotion in my voice, very sweetly and very brightly,

"You will be very pleased with me, Mother dear.

I have done just what you asked me to do.

I have thrown out all that old junk."

Europe and the impossible management of energetic security

Cosmin Gabriel Pacuraru

ISBN: 1497378877
ISBN-13: 978-1497378872

For who those who opened my eyes

I praise myself with having many friends, but there are few of them who would get out of bed at 3 in the morning to help me...this book is dedicated to them! If they read these lines, they will know who they are and will be in good thoughts.

The book is also dedicated to those who supported me along the way: family, friends that have no idea that I write books- my childhood friends and the ones who I meet in Bucharest's bars and discuss about everything and nothing without getting bored.

CONTENTS

Many thanks   5

1   Divergent strategies of energetic security   6

2   Security terms understood differently   9

3   USSR's energetic industry: determinant factor in international relations   13

4   The new Russian strategy   16

5   Energetic strategies in the geostrategic context   20

6   The impossibility of a common energetic strategy from the EU   23

7   Conclusions   27

8   Bibliography   28

Many thanks

Here we would have a long list… Those who explained the security, environment, and security risk terms to me…and they are many! The professors who guided me had an essential role because a journalist's superficiality is surpassed by and academician's stringency. First of all I would like to shake the hands of those from the Babeș-Bolyai University in Cluj-Napoca for trusting in me. Secondly, the colleagues who opened my curiosity for the notions with which I bumped into. Last but not least, my friends from the academic environment that sent me back to learn more and to whom I am thankful for!

1 Divergent strategies of energetic security

In the last months, Barosso's II Commission efforts to realize a common energetic strategy are blown away by Germany who changed its relationship and energetic strategy with Russia. The Bundestag voted to stop using nuclear energy until 2022, expressing their fear of a potential accident similar to the one in Fukushima.

But things are not as they seem! Let's not forget that beginning with the 60's, Germany, at that time The Federal Republic of Germany, began to make great business deals in the energetic domain with the Soviet Union. Even from those days, the Kremlin discovered the power it possesses: natural gas resources. Afterwards, France, Austria, and Italy changed their external politics strategy towards USSR. Until 1990 it was simple: there was the hunger for technology and the money necessary to sustain the state and the war in Afghanistan, and on the other hand, the necessity of industrial development sustained by a growing use of energy, made the ideologic and politic barriers easily passable, to the despair of the United States, the most important NATO member.

After the fall of the USSR and especially after the rise of Vladimir Putin, the Russian external politics was oriented to winning political influence and the direct economic advantages in the countries that import or transit Russian gas. In the new strategy, elaborated under the eyes of Vladimir Putin, are highlighted the most important ways of action:[1]

1. European Union countries to become increasingly dependent of Russian gases
2. Gigantic investments in pipelines
3. Market diversification by extending their exports to China.
4. Increasing the transport capacity in the ex USSR countries: Turkmenistan, Kazakhstan, Uzbekistan, and Azerbaijan to the Occident
5. creating intermediary firms in the occidental countries that sees about the gas imports
6. Associating Gazprom with "old business partners" in a variety of firms
7. Acquisition of or shareholding in a large number of gas production and distribution firms or producers of railways for the extraction industry and transport of gas or

---

[1] Kupchinsky, Roman - GAZPROM'S EUROPEAN WEB, Jamestown Foundation Library, Jamestown 2009, page 2

6

infrastructural firms (communications, railways, etc) from as many European countries possible, especially Union countries in exchange of a smaller gas price.

Applying the "follow the money" idea, we see the existence of a great lack of transparency not only in the commercial schemes of gas export but also in banking, recovering the resulting money, that don't always return to Gazprom implicit to Russia.

Analyzing the activity of intermediary firms and the persons implicated in these volatile companies, we can conclude that Russia follows infiltration of influential agents in all the structural political decisions of countries, European institutions, and firms that signs commercial accords, reaching to the ownership of important participations in transnational firms. [2]

Likewise, Russia does not expose to any state and Russian companies do not compromise with any company. The transaction position is always superior to those who Russia is doing business with, trying to impose solutions that are not to the advantage of the importer. [3]

Looking back in the last years, it is becoming clear that Russia is trying at any price to influence the national politics of all the European states by: control over the energetic resources, access to the energy market, control over transport routes of gas and petrol and dominating the opposition[4], in which we add acquiring companies that offer a monopoly position or at least an oligopoly in various important economic branches.

At this moment, the "energetic pliers" policy is put in action by Russia, its main partners being Germany (North Stream) and Italy (South Stream). [5] The existence of the pipelines that feed gas to West Europe, which transit countries like Ukraine and Byelorussia (with a political instability potential), the Baltic Countries and Poland (each with a moderate anti-Russian policy) is completed by North Stream, whose target is to boost Russian economic influence especially in Germany, Denmark, and the South Countries and also dimming the European influence for the transit countries. We also add South Stream in this equation.

In this equation, Russia's influence enters over the policies of the countries and communities implicated in the alternative European projects: Nabucco and AGRI. This influence is

[2] Kupchinsky, Roman - GAZPROM'S EUROPEAN WEB, Jamestown Foundation Library, Jamestown 2009, page 2
[3] http://www.sfin.ro/articol_9649/cat_de_tare_ne_permitem_sa_suparam_rusia.html sau
http://www.sigurantaenergetica.ro/wp-content/uploads/2009/05/Cat-de-tare-ne-permitem-sa-suparam-Rusia.doc – Cat de tare ne permitem sa ne suparam cu Rusia – Cosmin Pacuraru
[4] Dr. VOLOȘIN, Andriy – XXI CENTURY ENERGETIC WARS, Regional Stability and Security, "Universitatii Nationale de Aparare CAROL I" Publishing, Bucharest, 2009
[5] MANKOF, Jeffry - Eurasian energy security – Council on Foreign Relations, febr 2009, pag 14

observed in Turkey's position (which uses Russian gas in a proportion of 76% of the necessary through Blue Stream), in Bulgaria's position (which is included in the South Stream project), and in Germany's position (through the RWE company with which Gazprom is associated with in a couple of firms).

2 Security terms understood differently

Taking in account the definition of *threat*[6], understood from the perspective of *national security* "someone's or something's action that has the potential of interfering with national interests" from which we can come up with the term *"security politics* which should be deduced from analyzing the threats that generate positive reactions to reduce the harm done by these threats"[7], we can affirm that the European Union and implicitly Romania are under energetic threat of the independent policies carried out by Germany and Italy, being in correspondence with that of Russia's, which is the main political influence from the monopolist position of producer and transporter of raw materials.

This position reveals EU countries to risks and vulnerabilities. Economic threats of the internal stability of a state in conditions that some states follow economic strategies based on maximization of profits, monopoly formation, combining economics with politics, leading to geopolitical off balances which can degenerate into conflicts. These threats need to be tracked down, analyzed and stopped.

"Economic defense hearken back to state institutions that have their components settled through laws appropriate to this domain of activity. It follows the production and circulation of resources, diminishing national competition in a globalized economy, defending the data base and technological transfers, combating illicit exploitations of brevets, disinformation and counterfeiting."[8]

The European Commission understood that "on an economic basis, collective defense can contribute to the ratings rise of a country, the elevation of trust for strategic foreign investments in establishing the business area in the respective country, to improve the

---

[6] IONESCU, Voichiţa, Latin-Romanian dictionary, Ed. II, Orizonturi Publishing, f.a., p. 132

[7] ROBINSON, Paul "Dictionary of International Security" –C&A Publishing, Cluj Napoca, 2010, page 17

[8] Dr. MOŞTOFLEI. Constantin, Dr. DUŢU, Petre- COLLECTIVE DEFENCE and NATIONAL DEFANCE, "Universităţii Naţionale de Apărare" Publishing, Bucharest, 2004

exchange of goods and services with foreign partners"[9]. The characteristics of collective defense are: voluntary character, selectivity, open character, permittivity, organized character, judicial basis, legitimacy, discouragement.

Thus, taking in account the common interests and passing over egocentric economical interests of multinational companies, EU countries, especially in the second term of the Barroso Commission, have started to elaborate common defense policies. The European energetic strategy is a document that highlights the collective defense strategies in the energetic domain of the Union's countries and nearby ones of potential pressures exercised by Russia and the transit states (Ukraine, Byelorussia, and Moldova)

In today's conjuncture, whilst the international system is made up of states and other international actors in a circuit of political, military, and economic relations, the economic security is given not only by the actor's economic security and of the supply and undoing market and the transportation security.

We have three ways of approaching economic security:
-        Conservatory: in which the economic security is part of national security and state politics.
-        Liberal: in which eliminates the state's intervention and considers that the market should ripen and operate independently.
-        Socialist: in which takes in consideration the justice system and social equality intervening in the economy when social off balances are produced. [10]

In the last years, in the conjuncture of market globalization and growth of big international concerns, the span of east-European economies, ex-communist, and even the Russian expansionist economic policies, we can observe a redefining of the economic security concept through the eyes of the reference between the native and foreign property on natural resources and transportation. The countries that had a liberal approach on the economic growth by selling or granting resources, redefine their economic security policies, especially the energetic security ones.

---

[9] Dr. MOŞTOFLEI. Constantin, Dr. DUŢU, Petre- COLLECTIVE DEFENCE and NATIONAL DEFANCE, "Universităţii Naţionale de Apărare" Publishing, Bucharest, 2004

[10] SAVA, Ionel Nicu – Security studies; "Centrului Roman de Studii Regionale" Publishing, Bucharest, 2005, page 233

The energetic security of a state is integrated in the national security doctrine. Taking in account the principle of collective security, European Union countries, North Atlantic Treaty members, and the ex-USSR countries from the Caucasus elaborated common energetic strategies on moderate and long terms[11]. At this year's beginning, Russia had remade its energetic strategy. We can deduce that there is a new tendency in international relations in consequence of consciousness (by the political forces of every state) that the fact that energy has become a currency and a risk factor over national and regional security. Taking in consideration recent history, with examples of monopolization of economic domains by exterior forces, we can consider that energetic security is closely tied to the economic security and infrastructural security of ones state.

Economic security can be reduced to relevant problems in a practical point of view:
- the state's capacity to maintain independent production units in a global market
- the state's capacity to gain access to energetic sources and strategic material
- the eventuality that the economic dependency on the international market is used for touching political purposes
- the possibility that the global market would rise economic off balances between states
- the risk of economic globalization which results to diminishing economic functions of a state to generate a subterranean economy, illicit commerce, illicit technology traffic, affecting our environment
- the risk that the global economy would enter in a crisis due to wrong economic policies, weak political governance, weak international institutes, financial instability. [12]

In the last period the main discussion is about the possible *energetic threat* making reference to Russia or the Russian economic organizations more or less under the direct control of the Russian state, having connotations and references to the *intelligence and security* zone.

In the 90's, the European states were under the control of the left wing political forces, of social-democratic orientation and where the *citizen's security* was the national policy. In the year 2000, when Vladimir Putin came to power, the Russian Federation entered a period of economic "recharge" which goes to the retrace of foreign politics based on doctrines which bring are very similar with the imperialistic ones in the tsarist and soviet periods. This fact made the EU countries to reevaluate the definition of national security, putting accent on state and regional security, renouncing the citizen's security doctrines.

---

[11] CHIFU, Iulian, SAULIUC, Adriana, NEDEA Bogdan- Energy Security Strategies in the Wider Black Sea Region, "Curtea Veche" Publishing, Bucharest 2010

[12] SAVA, Ionel Nicu – Security studies; "Centrului Roman de Studii Regionale" Publishing, Bucharest, 2005, page 233

If we analyze Poland's position, which in the 90's sold 100% of the actions of the national gas distributor to Gazprom, on the criteria that the polish citizen will benefit of lower prices at the thousand cubic meters (the polish industry benefited of this facility, which at the end falls to the small cost prices of the produces that incorporate a large quantity of energy), we can say that today, Gazprom's dominating position in the polish economy is very disturbing. Taking notice of the introduction of the new extraction technologies of schist gasses, of the fact that Poland holds an enormous reserve of schist gas which can effect the Russian energetic monopoly exercised over the European countries[13] and the fact that the American company Amoco, the detainer of the extraction of the extraction technology, closed with the polish authorities an extraction contract, we can analyze the difficult position that the polish government is put in, being unable to distribute its own gasses to its citizens or to neighboring countries.

Another case study is the PR campaign sustained by the Gas de France society in Bucharest that sustains the idea that individual apartment heating systems reduce the consume of citizen's gas, an unreal fact proven and demonstrated in cities uncoupled in total from the central heating systems, where production costs for heated water are 2-2.5 times higher than cities that benefit of central heating systems. This action is in fact an energetic security threat to the Bucharest metropolitan zone and a threat to the material safety of the citizen. The campaign unwound in April- May of 2011, using personalized letters and premium influential written press, which wrote boasting articles to the individual apartment heating systems. The campaign's motive is that of feeding the national energetic dependence (more than 10% of the homes located in Bucharest) as a result of the rise of gas consummation and having the objective of profit maximization of the distributing company (GdF) and the import companies under the control of Gazprom.

In this way, we can conclude the following: ones state security should account for the regional security and include the citizen's security component

---

[13] http://business.timesonline.co.uk/tol/business/industry_sectors/natural_resources/article7087585.ece

3 USSR's energetic industry: determinant factor in international relations

Analyzing the relation between the Common State Market with USSR, we can affirm that the only criteria that worked were those of profit maximization. Even from the 60's, the foundation for cooperation of the largest German, French, or Italian firms was set with the soviet authorities with abiding by the COCOM's embargo accord (*Coordinating Committee for Multilateral Export Controls*- signed by NATO country members and had the role to establish common economic policies, inclusively lists of technologies and strategic equipment that are under the indirection of being exported east). Cooperation started through the Mannesmann and Phoenix Rheinruhr concerns that delivered steel pipes especially for the USSR, the first east-west pipe being inaugurated in 1973 at the border between Czechoslovakia and GFR, making GFR, by that year, Moscow's most important economic partner. The Christian-Democrat Party's and Chancellor's Konrad Adenauaer coming to power brought the respect of the NATO partner's agreements by suspending the commercial USSR contracts. Important companies such as (Salzgitter AG, Siemens, Haniel, IG Farben, Thyssen, Hoechst, and AEG) immediately cancelled their sponsorship of this party, resulting the social-democrat's coming to power lead by Willi Brandt, the founder of "Realpolitik", a term that redefines a new vision in the commerce with USSR. The term is immediately borrowed by the Italians and Austrians, that begin to import Russian gas through TAG I and TAG II pipes with ENI (89%) and OMV (11%) as shareholders[14].

Knowing the problems Hungary (Hungarian revolution-1956) and Czechoslovakia (Spring at Prague-1968) overtook in relation with USSR, GFR signs one of the biggest commercial contracts: Siberia Pipe – West Europe, in value of 1.2 billion marks and the IGAT I Pipe (Iranian Gas Trunkline) which transformed the USSR in an important transporter. The result was that the commerce between the Common Market and USSR doubled in only 3 years.

With the petrol crisis in 1973, industrialized European states were orienting toward natural gasses, especially the Russian ones, making the last generation technology (automatic equipment and know-how) to arrive in the Soviet Union. This way, the first pipe connecting

---

[14] http://grtgaz-deutschland.de/content/netz-veroeffpflichten/kundenportal2/actionarrien-index_uk.php

Siberia with France is put in function, the MEAGAL Pipeline with EON (51%), GDF Suez (44%) and OMV (5%) as shareholders[15]. But the automatic equipment imported to the USSR is used to perfect the SS20 rockets which are directed to West Europe in 1977. Even after the beginning of the War in Afghanistan and the Syndicate Revolts in Poland, the Common Market states seals the biggest contract ever signed with the USSR: " the contract of the century- the Siberia-Europe Gazoduct" which connected the largest gas storage facility Urengoi-Ujgorod and West Europe, with a pipeline of 5400 km that would permit an upgrade in the gas volume imported from 25 to 40 billion cubic meters per year and would have in mind Italy, Belgium, Holland, Switzerland, and Greece as potential clients.

In that period, the use of Russian gas in GFR reached up to 20%, in Austria to 67%, in France to 14%, and in Finland to 100%. There needs to be reminded that in that period the iron smelting industry was in recession and unemployment was rising. Pressures were made by Mannesmann, Benteler, Vallourec, Dalmine, and British Steel, for a contract of 5400 km of pipeline (20 million tons of steel), meaning profit. At this, the pumping station construction technology and the electronic material of the installations were added. The CIA's calculations show that the foreign bills obtained by the USSR could cover without a problem the Red Army's expenses in Afghanistan.

In that period, CIA annalists forwarded some material to the European desks explaining to them the dependency danger of USSR's energy, offering them the possibility to apply political and strategic pressure. But the naivety of the French and German surpassed any imagination: the banks loaned the USSR with millions of dollars (loans guaranteed by the two states), these being refundable in natural gas. This made the two states even more dependent through the risk of a banking system crisis[16]. The administration in Kremlin negotiated very well: 11 dollars for a thousand cubic meters for an even bigger energetic dependency for Europe and the possibility of a price rise in a 10 year future.

At the moment, the dual speech of the 4 European states (GFR, France, Italy, and Austria) was becoming more and more visible: on the first hand they were criticizing USSR for their policies in Afghanistan and Poland, for their arms policy and not respecting the human rights, and on the second hand, encouraging the large corporations to sign contracts with USSR and to furnish technology (which was under US license and was defying any embargo).

---

[15] http://business.timesonline.co.uk/tol/business/industry_sectors/natural_resources/article7087585.ece
[16] Source: http://grtgaz-deutschland.de/content/netz-veroeffpflichten/kundenportal2/actionarrien-index_uk.php

In 1980, the US started a plan to kneel the soviet economy. Starting off from the fact that USSR is sustaining its state from the foreign bills won from export of petrol and natural gas, the strategy being to lower the price of petrol and gas on the global market. This way, Saudi Arabia rose their production 4 times and the price of petrol dropped from 30$/baril to 12$/baril. This made that in 1986; USSR's bay balance had a deficit of 1.4 billion dollars, a year ago having a surplus of 700 million dollars, in the situation where natural gas production soared to 587 billion metric cubes per year[17]. This economic off-balance brought to one of the biggest food crisis USSR has ever seen, the government not even being able to import grain (30% of the consume was due to import) and to rationalize food consumption. The new administration represented by Mihail Gorbaciov was unable to manage the economic crisis that was slowly transforming into a political crisis, which brought to the fall of the USSR. The USSR's debt soared from 28 billion $ in 1986 to 54 billion $ in 1989.

---

[17] OUGARTCHINSKA, Roaumiana, CARRE, Jean Michel, Razboiul Gazelor – Amenintarea Rusa, Timisoara, Editura Antet, 2008, pag. 39

4 The new Russian strategy

In the extraction, stocking, and transport of gas industry, the Soviet Union left behind 160.000 km of pipelines, 350 pressing stations and dozens of gas storage facilities, located in the new-formed republics: Russia, Byelorussia, Ukraine, Kazakhstan, Turkmenistan, Uzbekistan, Kirghistan, Tajikistan, Armenia, and Moldova.

At that time (not taking in consideration the newly-discovered reserves) approximately 80% of the gas reserves were in Russia, 10% in Turkmenistan, the rest in Ukraine and the Caspic zone.

The problem was that 25% of the pipelines were in Ukraine (32.000 km with 120 pressing and pumping stations) and 13 immense gas storage facilities. This reality made Ukraine become the biggest importer of gas (30 billion cm/year) and the most important transit country: 100 billion cm, representing the occidental countries' export. Knowing that 80% of Russia's total export was gas, Russia had to control the entire infrastructure inherited from the USSR. This fact came true at the Alma Ata meeting made up of presidents from ex-USSR countries, which would soon form ISC- the Independent States Community- in 1991. This trail to manage actives in ex-USSR states failed to be put in motion, these being transferred in 1992 to the newly financed TurkmenGazprom and UkrGazprom[18].

The Yeltzin era along with the "mass privatization" of Russian companies represents a defining period for the new Russian economy order. We have a couple of direction to analyze: vertical economic reorganization, shift from patrimony to the extraction industry's private sector and the appearance of oligarchies. The privatization program in Russia ends in 1992. It can described in this way: every Russian citizen 18+ receives a 10.000 rubles voucher, subscribing to one of the societies waiting to be privatized. There are two new policies formed in the energetic domain: one for the petrol industry and another for the gas industry.

A couple of national and regional colossal energetic companies are built that hold the extraction, transport, and processing wings. The biggest societies are LukOil, TNK, Rosneft,

---

[18] OUGARTCHINSKA, Roaumiana, CARRE, Jean Michel, Razboiul Gazelor – Amenintarea Rusa, Timisoara, Editura Antet, 2008, pag. 41

and Yukos. The coupon subscribing is deliberately delayed for the working-class citizen, so they cannot use it. The coupon "black market" appears. At this moment the "oligarchy" class that intuited the "privatization" potential clotted and through the investment banks that they founded started to organize a "gray market", the acquisition price soaring up to 10% of the nominal value. Later, these privatization coupons were used so the handful of new business people could detain control over the petrol extraction industry firms. It's a well-known fact that along with petrol, natural gas is also extracted, but the proportion of gas extraction is too minute, the societies having a ponder just below 5%.

Viktor Chernomyrdin, the prime minister at that time and ex-second minister of gasses and first director of Gazprom protected this concern throwing out laws to fiscal facilities especially for him.

Vladimir Putin's coming to Kremlin was a milestone in Russia's external politics and implicitly in the internal politics and also total control of the energetic companies. In this period the development principles of extraction, transport, export, and foreign politics have been traced, revealed in the first page of this text.

From the geopolitical analysis, Russia began to develop ways around Ukraine. This analysis showed to be true after the gas crisis generated by Ukraine in 2005, followed by the one in 2008. There were realized new pipeline routes: Blue Stream which ties Turkey and Russia, BBL Pipeline that connects Holland to Great Britain, North Stream Pipeline that ties Russia and Germany (under the Baltic Sea, circling around the Baltic countries, Ukraine and Byelorussia, dimming their role in foreign regional politics), South Stream- which is still in the planning stage- that connects Russia with the EU countries (under the Black Sea, circling around Ukraine).

Starting with 2009, when the financial crisis deeply affected European industries, the off-balance between offer and demand, the offer becoming larger than the demand. The dynamicity of the energy market is becoming more and more unforeseeable. The specialists' previsions from the Oxford Institute for Energy Studies in 2006 showed a decline in demand an implicitly in the gas extraction. This prevision was also made by the Center of International and Strategic Studies in Washington, as in Image 1:

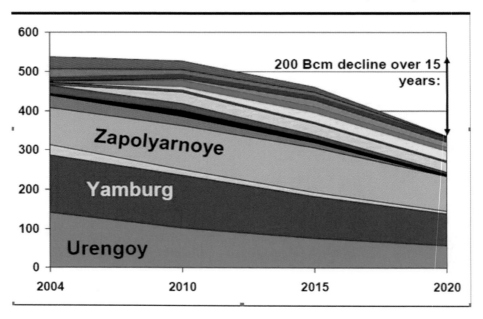

Image 1: The production decline of Russian gas Source: The Future of Russian gas and Gazprom, pr. Jonathan Stern, director Gas Research of Oxford Institute, Centre of Strategic and International Studies, Washington DC, 2006

In the same study[19], it is foreseen that the independent producers would develop by raising their production. This prevision could remain valid for the petrol industry's "big 4": LukOil, Rosfnet, and Yukos, the other smaller companies, not having their own pipeline distribution network, could be swallowed[20] by the colossal Gazprom.

In the crisis' last three years, Russia was powerfully hit by the fact that its gas exports have

[19] OUGARTCHINSKA, Roaumiana, CARRE, Jean Michel, Razboiul Gazelor – Amenintarea Rusa, Timisoara, Editura Antet, 2008, pag. 53
[20]pr. STERN, Jonathan (director Gas Research of Oxford Institute) – The Future of Russian Gas and Gazprom Washington DC, Centre of Strategic and International Studies, 2006, pag. 3

fallen by almost 20% in 2009, not forgetting that 80% of Russian exports represent natural gas and that they have a big contribution in Russia's GDP.

Analyzing the gas price variation which has no relation with the global crisis, but only with the regional political crisis and here we are referring to the two major leaps in 2005 and 2008 that intervened after the misunderstandings between Ukraine and Russia (revealed in Image 2), we can appreciate that in this context, Russia's need for funds could result another gas crisis which would automatically result to soaring prices.

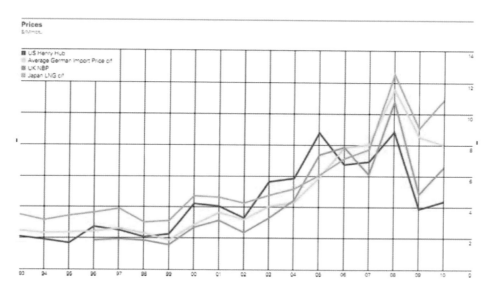

Image 2: Price variation around the world Source: 60 years BP Statistical Review World Energy, pag 27

5 Energetic strategies in the geostrategic context

The International Energy Agency's previsions say that in 2000, a third of EU's energy consumption came from Russian gasses, and in 2008 EU countries were importing 40% of the necessary, and in 2030, the import is said to reach a milestone of 66%[21]. The numbers show that the demand rises by 1.5% per year.

Starting with 2004, along with the founding of the European Commission lead by Jose Emanuel Barroso, the first trials were made to create a common European energetic strategy. The energetic problems commissioner, Andris Piebalgs, Lithuania, representative, did not accord too much attention to the alternative energy that began to take shape in southern Europe, projects meant to totally eliminate the dependency of Russian gas imports. In this period, the idea of importing gas from other sources appeared: the Caspian Countries and the Middle East. Some south-east European countries along with Turkey conceived the Nabucco and AGRI projects. Delay reasons for this common strategy exists, implicitly in the design and construction: the financial crisis and the great production companies of railway material and the banks already invested in the North Stream project, today, being in the finalization stage and it is said to cover for the next few years the European energy necessity.

In the Caspic geopolitical equation, some modifications intervened even from the middle 90's when the American firms penetrated on the petrol and natural gas extraction market in the Caspic Sea and the Russian riparian zones, and in the ex-USSR countries considered by Kremlin to be under the influential sphere: Azerbaijan, Georgia, Armenia, Kazakhstan, and Turkmenistan. The countries that warmed their relations with the US and the EU countries automatically had their relations with Russia cooled. Political and interethnic tensions rose, that brought to the separation of the South Ossetia territory, in Georgia's case[22]. The outcome is that the Azerbaijan, Georgian, and Armenian administrations warmed more and more to the US and the UE countries, signing various treaties and political and economical

---

[21] The transport price imposed by Gazprom for the independent companies was of 0.84$ cm/km and for Russia and the ISC countries 0.92$/cm/km

accords with the two important players, most of them tied to the energetic sector collaboration.

Starting off from the production soar and gas transport for the Caspic area potential; (Turkmenistan - 80 billion cm/year. Kazakhstan- 50 billion cm/year, Uzbekistan- 25 billion cm/year), the European Union appreciated that in the energetic equation, this area is very important. If we take in account the acquisition price at the border by Russia of furnished gas from these countries, prices varying between 65$ and 110$ for 1000 cubic meters in the situation where Russia re-exports today with prices that sometimes exceed 450$ for 1000 cubic meters, we can conclude that the EU offer is much more advantageous than the Russian one. Adding the fact that these countries could become propitious markets for European goods, the European Union's interests for collecting diplomatic and commercial relation with these countries has grown.

Kremlin intuited the new EU direction and the Putin Government elaborated in the course of 2010, a new energetic strategy with the main course of action in the foreign politics: Gazprom should acquire, or become a shareholder in energetic, transport and utilities companies in the entire world[23].

Comparing the sell price of gas and the political and economic pressures applied to the important countries by Russia; this way Byelorussia was importing in 2007 gas with 46$ for 1000 cubic meters in the situation that the national distributor, BelTranzGaz has 50% shareholder Gazprom and the majority of the Byelorussian economic domains have Russian shareholders. In 2005, Moldova was buying gas with 110$ for 1000 cubic meters and in 2006 with 160$, at half price than the European states. In 2007, when the Tarlev government wished a participation growth for the Moldavian state to more than 50%, (the other 50% being Gazprom's), the price of imported Moldova Republic doubled to 300$ for 1000 cubic meters. Transnistria, Moldova's separatist region, imports gas at the declared price of 60$ for 1000 cubic meters, but because of this region, unpaid gas has accumulated in time, the debt climbing to 2 billion dollars. Until 2004, Ukraine paid under 200$ for 1000 cm but in 2005, Russia raised the price to 230$. Not liking this price, Ukraine unleashed a gas crisis. Today, Ukraine pays approximately 300$ for 1000 cm. Poland, having Gazprom as the absolute shareholder in the ex-national gas transport and distribution company, buys until 2008 gas with the price of 120$ for 1000 cm. And Germany has always been happy of the preferential

---

[23] Energetic Security- Actual preoccupation and of perspective for the North-Atlantic Alliance- Dr. Ioan Codrut Lucinescu, Alina Orescovici, National Defense University "Carol I", European Union security and defense, the anual scientific communication session with international participation, Bucharest, April 17-18 2008

gas prices. Until 2006, Germany paid 235$ for 1000 cm in the situation where the other European countries were paying around 300% for 1000 cm[24].

---

[24] Russian officials declarations chosen from the "Adevarul" and "Romania Libera" newspapers

(http://www.adevarul.ro/international/Razboiul-Georgia-provocat-serviciile-rusesti_0_29397412.html si http://www.romanialibera.ro/actualitate/mapamond/georgia-acuza-rusia-de-atentate-teroriste-227893.html)

6 The impossibility of a common energetic strategy from the EU

In the equation of coordinating energy strategies of the EU countries we have to take in account a minimum of two factors: the dependency rate of Russian gas (shown in the chart below) and each country's percentage from the total export of Russian gas

Chart: European Union countries' dependency of Russian gas

Country	Dependency rate
Bulgaria	100%
Slovakia	100%
Finland	100%
Estonia	100%
Lithuania	100%
Greece	100%
Denmark	100%
Belgium	100%
Lithuania	100%
Austria	75%
Czech Republic	75%
Hungary	75%
Poland	67%
Romania	52%
Slovenia	51%
Germany	42%
Italia	33%
France	23%
Holland	12%

Non EU states

Serbia	100%
Croatia	88%
Turkey	76%
Switzerland	12%

Sources: Eurostat- 2007 report, CRS- Report for Congress- The European Union' Energy Security Challenges, 2008, ECFR- Beyonf dependence, 2009

We can observe that half of the Union's countries have a large dependency rate, the percentage of Russian gas consumption being over 50%.

But not all countries are important in the pay balance resulting from Russian gas export.

We also need to analyze how dependent Russia is of gas export depending on the export size of every country and the money that it wins, as we see in Image 3:

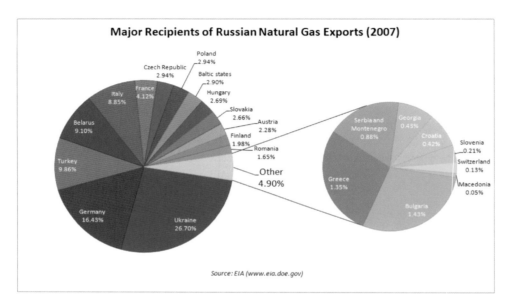

Image3: Russian gas export percentage- countries Source: EIA (US Energy Information Administration

We can observe that the sums collected by Russia from the gas-importing countries with an order of magnitude. If Germany occupies the most important spot (in the EU countries) followed by Italy, France, Poland, the Baltic Countries (all in one place), Hungary, Slovakia, and Austria, the others count less in the Russian foreign pay balance.

This results that Russia treats with a preferential degree of attention; Russia accords more attention to the countries that are over 3% in this ranking and accord less attention those under 3% of the total gas export. We can conclude that Russia wishes a different treatment for every country and resists the existence of a common European energy strategy that could disadvantage Russia.

In the Union's statistics show that 84% of gas consumption is represented by imports through pipelines in this order: 52% from Russia, 31% from Norway, 12% from Algeria, 3% from Libya, 2% from Iran[25]. Thereby, this shows that Russia needs to have an important spot in strategy building for the near future.

Analyzing the European energetic strategy draft elaborated by the Barosso Commission, we can conclude that there wishes to be a "release of the energetic pliers of North Stream and South Stream" through the two major energetic projects: Nabucco and AGRI (As seen in image 4).

---

[25] OUGARTCHINSKA, Roaumiana, CARRE, Jean Michel, Razboiul Gazelor – Amenintarea Rusa, Timisoara, Editura Antet, 2008, pag. 87 si KUPCINSKY, Roman - GAZPROM'S EUROPEAN WEB, Jamestown, Jamestown Foundation Library, 2009, pag 2

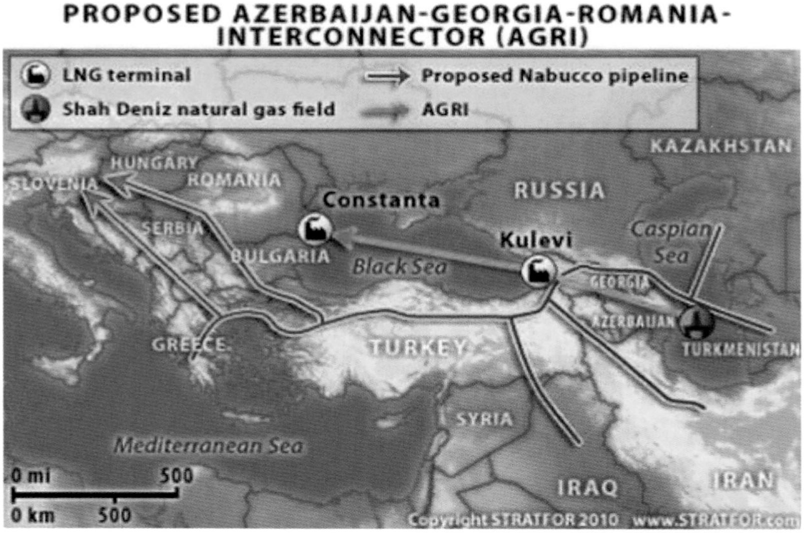

Image 4: Nabucco and AGRI routes. Source: STRAFOR

Analyzing Russia's attitude in the last few years, it is preparing to reduce exports to EU, confirming the European Commission's wish to detach the monopoly of Russian gas. This is deducted from Vladimir Putin's visit to China in 2006, where he signed a contract for two pipeline routes (which bypass Mongolia); a corridor parallel to the Pacific coast and another which passes through Turkmenistan, which will transport over 80 billion cm/year. Taking in account that these two new routes need time and money to be put in use, we conclude that in the last months, Russia is continuing its policy for the separation of the EU countries, offering advantages to Germany.

The conclusion is that the European Union cannot have in the near future, a common energetic policy, because of sometimes divergent interests of its component states and Russia's efforts in foreign politics to separate the European Union.

7 Conclusions

The first conclusion is that the European Union cannot have in the near future a common energetic policy because of the sometimes divergent interests of the composing states. The second motive of the impossibility of creating a common energetic policy is represented by Russia's efforts in foreign politics to separate the Union by discriminating the main gas importers, offering smaller prices in exchange for Russian investment possibilities in the respective countries.

Russia, knowing the gas and petrol dependency rate of European countries and the period of resource exhaustion, offered at the beginning of partnerships, advantageous energy contracts. After a period of time, after these states became dependent of imported Russian resources, Kremlin can adopt whenever it wants blackmail policy, like it did with a couple of countries already, having the following examples: acquisition of cell phone companies in some Caspic countries, Acquisitioning MOL- Hungary's main energetic company, NIS-Serbia's main energetic company, or imposing the construction of nuclear plants with Russian technology in Turkey and Bulgaria.

The only chance that the European Union can protect itself from future blackmail, is to elaborate and respect a common energetic strategy, leaving behind immediate national interests in the favor of common collective defense interests with an unlimited timeline.

In 2007, the European Commission elaborated the "European Energetic Policy" document that traces the most important ways of action, which include: competition assurance on the energy market, research development in the energetic domain, the use of alternative energy sources, and most important, the elaboration of a common energetic strategy for all the member states. If this document would transform into a European Commission decision, the common energetic security problem could be solved, all the member countries, and EU non-member countries, could be sheltered from a possible Russian shakedown.

8 **Bibliography**

Romania's national security strategy

The European Union's security strategy
National strategy for a durable economic development, MO 297/2000
WALTZ N. Kanneth– *The Theory of International Politics,* "Polirom" Publishing, Iasi 2007

MIROIU Andrei, UNGUREANU Radu Sebastian - *The Book of International Relations,* "Polirom" Publishing, Iasi 2006.

SAVA, Ionel Nicu – Security studies; "Centrului Roman de Studii Regionale" Publishing, Bucharest, 2005

pr. STERN Jonathan - The Future of russian gas and Gazprom, Centre of Strategic and International Studies, Washington DC, 2006

STRUMER, Michael – Putin & the New Russia, "Litera" Publishing, 2011, page 173 - 196

MORGENTHAU Hans J. – *Nations Politics. The fight for power and the fight for peace,* "Polirom" Publishing, Iasi, 2007.

Challenges at the security and strategy address at the beginning of the XXI century, History section, geopolitics and geostrategy, "Universitatii Nationale de Aparare" Publishing, Bucharest, 2005.

FUEREA Augustin, Guide to the European Union, "Univers Juridic" Publishing, Bucharest, 2004.

Martin Weight; The Power Policy, "Arc" Publishing, Bucharest, 1998

CLAVAL Paul, Geopolitics and geostrategy, "Corint" Publishing, Bucharest, 2002

GEOPOLITICS- Energetic resources asymmetry, Topform, 2008

HILHOR Constantin, CONTEMPORARY INTERNATIONAL SECURITY POLICY. ENERGETIC DOMAIN- "Institutul European" Publishing, 2008

GANGA, Daniela-Paula – European Union- Russia Relations. The Energetic Problem

KUPCINSKY, Roman- GAZPROM'S EUROPEAN WEB, *Jamestown, Jamestown Foundation*

Library, 2009

KUPCINSKY, Roman- Russian LNG- The Future Geopolitical Battleground, *Jamestown, Jamestown Foundation Library, 2009*

Maurice Vaisse, *Dictionary of international relations. Century XX,* "Polirom" Publishing, Iasi, 2008

Martin Griffiths, *International relations: schools, currents, thinkers,* „Ziua" Publishing, Bucharest, 2003

STRATFOR, ECFR Analysis

ABOUT THE AUTHOR

Even though he is an engineer as his basic profession, he has a master's degree in politics studies with a very odd subject: transactional analysis applied to political groups and a PhD in international relations with the subject: Romania's Energetic Security in the European context- the Gas chapter. Meanwhile, he benefited from an experience exchange in the United States, became specialized in transactional analysis, and participated in all sorts of specialized courses and trainings.

Cosmin Gabriel Păcuraru structurally speaking remains a journalist! His research comes from many places based on a main rule. Between 2001 and 2008 he wrote, lead newsrooms, and held top management functions. He realized consulting in the political, press management and marketing domains and trained many Romanian and Moldavian journalists in the news domain. Now he realizes communication consulting (his last important client being the World Health Organization), and has an audio-video recording studio, Positive Records, and practices the mediation profession.

From time to time he writes comments and analysis about the Romanian and Moldavian press and also has time to write books in specialized domains.

4247171R00020

Printed in Germany
by Amazon Distribution
GmbH, Leipzig